Growing Broadleaves

Growing Broadleaves

Silvicultural Guidelines for Ash, Sycamore, Wild Cherry, Beech and Oak in Ireland

P.M. Joyce

J. Huss   R. McCarthy

A. Pfeifer   E. Hendrick

ISBN 0 9523938 9 1

First published in 1998 by COFORD, National Council for Forest Research and Development, National University of Ireland, Belfield, Dublin 4

Production Co-ordinator Donal Magner

Designed at Language

Printed by McDonald & Glennon

Photographs:
J. Cooke, E. Hendrick, J. Huss, P.M. Joyce, R. McCarthy, R. Mullan, M. Spiecker

To Owen V. Mooney

Father of Irish forest research

Foreword

The first comprehensive prescriptions for the management of broadleaved woodlands in Ireland were published in May 1794 under the title 'A Practical Treatise on Planting and the Management of Woods and Coppices'. In the preface, author Samuel Hayes of Avondale, comments: "if thus I shall add but an individual to the cause of planting, or preserving of timber, I shall consider neither my own time nor that of my reader as unprofitably employed". COFORD, in presenting these guidelines, echoes these words, with the condition that the individual follows a silvicultural objective to grow high quality broadleaves.

Since the foundation of the State the planting of broadleaves has been limited both by the economics of broadleaf production and the unavailability of suitable land. Conifers have, therefore, dominated Irish forestry for most of the twentieth century. They were more adaptable to infertile sites, had shorter rotations, and yielded better economic returns. Furthermore, conifers had a much greater capacity to provide the resource needed for national timber requirements.

Developments within agriculture in the late twentieth century have given rise to conditions where broadleaves can be grown successfully. Oversupply in agricultural produce has released land that is now being planted with broadleaved species. However, the virtual absence of an indigenous broadleaved culture has deprived growers of the opportunity to acquire the requisite silvicultural expertise. Without this knowledge, the management of existing broadleaved plantations poses difficulties.

This book is intended to help redress this situation. It provides the forester, landowner and student with silvicultural guidelines for the establishment and treatment of broadleaves in Ireland. It brings together information on growth response of broadleaves within Ireland, supplemented where necessary by data from Britain and continental Europe. To enhance our knowledge, practising foresters and growers are exhorted to experiment and record their experiences. Over time these will provide the data needed to consolidate, adapt and update our knowledge of broadleaved silviculture.

The guidelines cover the following species: ash, sycamore, wild cherry, beech, and oak. The order of presentation accords with their rotation lengths. The omission of other species is dictated largely by the paucity of information on their growth and yield. Sweet chestnut shows good growth potential but its occurrence is confined mainly to isolated trees or scattered groups. Alder, birch, lime and elm are considered only in mixtures.

Broadleaved silviculture arguably has the longest time horizon of any land-based enterprise in Ireland. Yet the present grants and premiums are structured on a 20 years period when most broadleaved stands have only reached the tending stage. Provision must be made for continuing support beyond this period, through the uneconomic early thinning stage. This is essential if the quality targets outlined in these guidelines are to be realised.

COFORD has great pleasure in presenting these guidelines. The work has involved considerable effort by many project participants. These guidelines represent long hours of 'off camera' work, free-time debate and unparalleled dedication to achieving a landmark in Irish forest history. Like all good landmarks they usually point to a better route. Ignore them and we could be in a silvicultural cul-de-sac. Follow them and we can avoid the obvious obstacles and allow us to pass a new woodland resource to future generations.

Fergal Mulloy
Director
April 1998

Acknowledgements

We gratefully acknowledge the funding provided by COFORD to undertake this study on broadleaves.

Many people have helped in various ways during the preparation of these guidelines. We acknowledge with pleasure the contributions and help of the following:

Dr Wendy Walsh for permission to reproduce drawings of the leaf characteristics and seed of the different species; Professor Dr F.H. Schweingruber, Swiss Federal Institute for Forest, Snow and Landscape Research for permission to reproduce photographs of microscopic wood anatomy; Herr Germar Csapek, University of Freiburg, who prepared the figures for ash, sycamore, beech and oak; Ms S. Wilbourne, Cork University Press for permission to reproduce Figure 3.1 from the Atlas of the Irish Rural Landscape; Mr P. Doody, Coillte who provided information on seed collection and storage; Dr K. Clancy, UCD for information on soil bacteria and fungi; Mr S. Heaney, Coillte for supplying specimens of ash, sycamore, cherry, beech and oak; Dr M. Keane, Coillte for access to research data on ash spacing experiments; Mr J. Ronan Joyce for translating literature on the silviculture of broadleaves from French; Dr Á. Ní Dhubáin, UCD who made available relevant literature on timber properties of the species; members of the *ad hoc* Consultative Group who provided advice and support, Mr M. Bulfin, Teagasc; Mr J. Connelly, Forest Service; Professor J. J. Gardiner, UCD; Mr M. Doyle, Dr M. Keane and Mr J. Neilan, Coillte.

We are indebted to those who made it possible for us to visit broadleaved stands in other countries and obtain information on the silviculture and management of the relevant species. We express our gratitude to:

Our colleagues in the Northern Ireland Forest Service, Mr W. Wright, Mr P. Hunter-Blair, Mr C. Farmer, Mr S. Morwood, Mr I. Wright-Turner and Mr M. Clements with whom we toured the broadleaved forests of Northern Ireland and who readily provided growth data on ash; Mr. R. Blackiston-Huston, Factor at the Caledon Estate, Northern Ireland; Dr G. Peterken for discussions about broadleaved ecology in the Forest of Dean; Dr G. Mayhead, University of Wales (Bangor) for discussion about the role of broadleaves in British forestry; Dr. P. S. Savill, University of Oxford for providing a tour of Bagley Wood and discussion about the silviculture of oak and the natural regeneration of ash and sycamore; Messrs. George and Paul Stevenson for a tour of the sycamore plantations at Bolton Hall, Yorkshire and discussion about the silviculture of the species; *Mme*. B. Pilard-Landeau of the *Office National des Forêts*, STIR *Nord-Ouest* and *M*. N. Le Goff of INRA, Nancy for arranging a tour of broadleaved forests in France and providing valuable information on developments in broadleaved research; Mr A. Jørgensen, *Skov-og Naturstyrelse*, Denmark for arranging a visit to beech and oak forests in Denmark and providing information on their growth and regeneration.

Lastly, we wish to express our thanks to Dr M. Keane and Dr P. S. Savill, who kindly took the time to read an early draft and made many helpful suggestions.

Padraic M. Joyce
Maurice Kennedy Research Centre
University College Dublin

Jürgen Huss
Institute of Silviculture
University of Freiburg

Richard McCarthy
Coillte Research and Development
Newtownmountkennedy

Alistair Pfeifer
Coillte Research and Development
Newtownmountkennedy

Eugene Hendrick
COFORD

Contents

Introduction

HISTORICAL BACKGROUND

As the ice-sheets retreated northwards at the end of the last glaciation period some 10,000 years ago, Ireland began to be colonised by trees migrating from the Continent. Ash and elm migrated across Britain into Ireland while oak, alder and pine are thought to have come across a landbridge from western France through what is now the Bay of Biscay and Celtic Sea. Beech and sycamore failed to reach this country before the landbridges disappeared and their presence here is the result of importations some centuries ago.

Between 5,000 and 7,500 years ago woodland probably covered 80% of the land surface of Ireland. The broad distribution of species consisted of the main tree species such as alder, ash, birch, elm, oak, as well as pine, and minor species including hazel, holly, juniper, wild cherry, willow and yew. Elm and hazel dominated the better midland soils; oak flourished on the more acid soils of the south and north-east, and pine colonised the more exposed acid soils of the west. Towards the end of the period (*c.* 5000 BP[1]) neolithic farmers began a limited clearance but their impact on the forests, which had persisted for 1,500 years or more, was minimal. This period was the warmest since the last glaciation, with a mean summer temperature some 2°C higher than at present and a longer growing season. It ended with the 'elm decline', resulting in a widespread decrease in elm. This coincided with the first real impact of man on the natural woodlands.

As the population increased during the Bronze Age (4500-2500 BP), agricultural pressure on the better soils became more widespread. The development of blanket bog during this time was probably due to a combination of human activity and climatic change. The climate became wetter and cooler; peat bogs spread, and pine, birch and oak forests were overwhelmed. Their remnants remain as 'bog oak' and 'bog deal' in the midland and western peatlands to this day. Pine disappeared from most of the country about this time, although it may have survived in isolated locations in the south west for a further 2,000 years. Man contributed significantly to the destruction of the forest during the subsequent Iron Age, which commenced about 2500 BP, when large scale clearances of woodland were made.

Oak was by far the most widespread species, as the number of place names with "derry" would suggest, but the oak population seems to have been subject to a good deal of fluctuation. A chronology of oak timbers over the last two millennia shows periods of abundance in the 6th, 7th and 12th centuries and again in the 15th and 16th centuries. These are separated by periods of scarcity in the 9th, 14th and late 17th centuries. As the population increased, changes in agricultural practice from pastoral to tillage could have hastened clearance but these are largely unrecorded. However, a Welsh traveller to Ireland in 1185 comments that "there are many woods and marshes; here and there, there are some fine plains but in comparison with the woods they are indeed small".

The popular belief that Ireland still had substantial areas of ancient oak forest at the beginning of the 17th century, is subject to controversy among authors. It is agreed, however, that what woodland was there was heavily overexploited during the period of unrest that followed. Commenting on the degree of this exploitation, Samuel Hayes of

---

[1] BP: Before present

1

Avondale wrote in 1794 that "such has been the waste of timber in Ireland during the last century from the unsettled state of the kingdom, and other causes, among which we may reckon the introduction of iron forges and furnaces, that there scarcely exists in some districts, a sufficiency to favour the supposition that we ever possessed a valuable growth".

The latter half of the 18th century saw an attempt, with considerable success, to restore the woodlands. By 1841 there were 140,000 ha of new plantations and the area under conifers had increased eightfold. However, the year 1880 marked the zenith of woodland area in private ownership. The following year saw the introduction of the first of a series of land acts, which would eventually result in a major change in land ownership. Conscious of their insecurity, the estate owners liquidated their timber assets and travelling sawmills moved across the country from estate to estate. The woodlands that survived were heavily exploited during World War I and only some 50,000 ha remained by the 1920s. These suffered further exploitation during World War II. Some were cleared of timber and converted to coniferous crops; many remain as overgrown coppice and degenerate remnants of former broadleaved woodlands.

1.2 POLICIES AND INCENTIVES FOR AFFORESTATION

The parlous state of native woodlands at the end of the 17th century gave rise to numerous acts of parliament to promote planting but with very limited success. Recognising that landowners needed some financial inducement, the Dublin Society (later the Royal Dublin Society) began, in 1741, to offer premiums (grants) for planting and to subsidise the propagation and sale of trees. This proved highly effective and by the turn of the 19th century at least 54,000 ha of plantations had been added to what native woodland survived. The premiums were supported by the Irish Parliament from 1761 but, after the Act of Union, the parliament at Westminster reduced this to a non-viable level. However, the practice of planting had been established and, up to the Famine, a further 85,000 ha of plantations had been added, to give a total plantation area of about 140,000 ha (1.7% of land area), in addition to what natural forest remained.

Reform of the structure of ownership in Irish agriculture began in the 1880s with the land acts, which arranged for the transfer of land from landlord to tenant. The Estate Commissioners, in buying an estate and reselling it to the tenants, were unable to manage incidental woodland and, in any event, the tenants had little interest in woodland: sawmillers remained the only outlet. By 1907 the estimated area of woodland had dwindled to 125,000 ha or 1.5% of the land area. This figure was shrinking rapidly and the quality of woodland was deteriorating.

Concern over the condition of woodland in the country led to the purchase of Avondale House and estate in 1904, thereby heralding the beginning of state investment in forestry. A few years later a committee set up to enquire and report as to the improvement of forestry in Ireland expressed strong support for state involvement. The capital outlay required and the continuity of management over a long period, as well as the economic and social benefits, were among the reasons given. The committee recommended the maintenance of the existing 125,000 ha of woodland, the creation of a similar area of state woodland and the planting by private owners to bring this up to 200,000 ha.

The outbreak of World War I changed the direction and tempo of forestry. Timber was needed and the estates were expected to supply it. There was no compulsion to replant felled areas and this position remained unchanged until 1930 when the Forestry Act of 1928 came into effect. At the establishment of the State some 7,000 ha passed to the Forestry Division. Land acquisition was a priority if forestry was going to expand. Furthermore, the policy was influenced by the government's desire to ensure that forestry did not encroach on agricultural land.

In 1925, the Minister for Agriculture in his address to the Dáil emphasised that it was not the policy of his department to acquire land for afforestation which could be used to form an agricultural holding or to augment an existing one. Furthermore, the maximum price the State was allowed to pay for land (£10/ha) for afforestation would ensure that this situation did not arise and Land Commission inspectors policed all land transfers. Although this price limit was doubled to £20/ha in 1949, the above policy of forest land acquisition remained in force until 1969, when land productivity criteria (yield class) were introduced in an attempt to provide some flexibility in the price paid for land. With entry to the European Economic Community (EEC) in the 1970s land prices soared and acquisition for forestry became extremely difficult. This situation continued into the early 1980s.

Land acquisition policy for forestry was to have considerable impact on land quality and species composition of state forests. Apart from the acquisition of some land suitable for broadleaves during the Economic War of the 1930s, the poor quality of forest land ensured that afforestation would consist almost entirely of coniferous species (about 95%). Furthermore, Sitka spruce and lodgepole pine would dominate (about 80%) among the conifers being planted. For most of the period broadleaves had a token presence of 3 - 5% of annual planting.

The first incentive to the private sector came in the form of a £10/ha planting grant under the 1928 Forestry Act. This level was raised periodically, but its attraction to landowners was minimal. Apart from a few notable exceptions the private sector showed very little interest in forestry until the mid 1980s, although the EEC sponsored Western Package, launched in 1981, was generous compared to earlier planting grants. However, by the late 1980s production restrictions in agriculture, coupled with payment of premiums in addition to planting grants, brought about the desired change. Annual private planting expanded rapidly from around 700 ha in 1985 to over 2,200 ha in 1986 and 17,300 ha in 1995, with farmers playing an ever increasing role.

The better land becoming available for forestry provides the opportunity to plant a greater range of species and it has become government policy that 20% of total annual afforestation will be of broadleaves. Furthermore, the proposed target afforestation for oak will be a minimum of 20% of broadleaved afforestation. This ambitious proposal is reflected in the increased grants and premiums for ash and sycamore and particularly for oak and beech. The effect of this government initiative has been a substantial increase in the area devoted to broadleaves in the private sector during the past five years.

1.3   BENEFITS

Woodlands produce many benefits such as the production of a great variety of timber assortments as well as the provision of environmental and socio-economic services. Of those, the economic production of wood has been the primary objective on sites suited to this purpose. This objective is stated explicitly in the Strategic Plan for the Development of the Forestry Sector in Ireland (1996).

Apart from the creation of a native hardwood resource, such a strategy will reduce our future dependence on tropical hardwoods and help to relieve the exploitation pressures on these forests. For over a century much of our supply of quality broadleaved timber has been met from tropical sources. Environmental concern has been expressed about the overexploitation and destruction of these forests so this supply may no longer be sustainable. In any event, many tropical countries are no longer content to export their timber in the raw state. This, combined with the scarcity factor, will undoubtedly have implications for temperate broadleaved timber supply and prices in future years.

Wood is not the only product of forests; they also provide various environments in which people can pursue different interests. Some of these benefits may give rise to conflicting demands and since they rarely pass through the market place they are more difficult to evaluate in terms of priority. Yet, in general, all have a high degree of compatibility with the sustained development of broadleaved timber production.

Broadleaved woodlands are a favourite location for recreation, including walking, horse riding and camping. There is also an increasing perception that woodland, particularly mixed and broadleaved woodlands of diverse age groups, enhances the quality of landscape. Woodland ecosystems offer the potential for the provision of environmental services such as watershed protection and the prevention of soil erosion, in addition to the conservation of genetic diversity.

Woodlands, both broadleaved and coniferous, play a significant role in carbon storage by absorbing atmospheric carbon dioxide during photosynthesis. Apart from a reduction in the use of fossil fuel, trees are the most important mechanism for limiting the increase in atmospheric concentrations of carbon dioxide. However, only forests that are undergoing net growth can sequester carbon and behave as a sink. In a mature forest, experiencing no net growth, no net sequestration of carbon occurs. Apart from economic criteria it is therefore important to regenerate old woodland if this important function is to be achieved. Young woodlands can be used to increase carbon sequestration and harvesting begins the process of woodland renewal.

Harvesting operations and wood based industries provide employment for people and enable them to remain in rural Ireland. Although harvesting is often regarded as an activity that is competitive with other benefits, such as recreation and landscape, it is an essential operation in managed woodland. If done judiciously and at strategic intervals, the differing age gradations can actually enhance the landscape with minimal effect on recreation.

Establishment of a forest represents an investment similar in many respects to any other financial undertaking but with one major difference, the time factor. Rotations for ash (except for hurleys) and sycamore range from 60 to 80 years, beech from 100 to 120 years and oak from 120 to 160 years or more. The relatively small harvesting volume, the long payback period, coupled with the fact that the main expenditure occurs at the establishment stage, makes the growing of broadleaves financially unattractive to the private investor were it not for grants and premiums.

Such grants and premiums are now available in adequate measure to defray the cost of broadleaved establishment. In disbursing these subventions, there is a responsibility to ensure the creation of a broadleaved resource for a future generation, in terms of timber supply and the associated environmental and socio-cultural unpriced benefits. Just as a previous generation has made sacrifices to bequeath to the present one a coniferous softwood forest resource, it, in turn, has an obligation to use the existing subventions wisely for the creation of a broadleaved resource for future generations.

Edmund Burke might well have been referring to Irish broadleaved woodland when he said: "A great unwritten compact exists between the dead, the living and the unborn. We leave to the unborn a colossal financial debt, perhaps inescapable, but incurred nonetheless in our time and for our immediate benefit. Such an unwritten compact requires that we leave to the unborn something more than debts and depleted natural resources. Surely, where natural resources can be utilised and at the same time perpetuated for future generations, what has been called 'constitutional morality' requires that we do so." [1]

---

[1] Quoted in U.S. Supreme Court case, *State* v. *Dexter* (1947). See Cubbage and Siegal in Bibliography.

2 *Silvicultural Strategies and Procedures*

2.1 NATIONAL STRATEGY

The stated goal of the Strategic Plan for the Development of the Forestry Sector in Ireland (1996) is: "To develop forestry to a scale and in a manner which maximises its contribution to national economic and social well-being on a sustainable basis and which is compatible with the protection of the environment." Within that goal it is proposed to expand afforestation levels to 25,000 ha/annum to the year 2000 and 20,000 ha/annum to year 2030. Furthermore, it is proposed that the target for broadleaved afforestation be maintained at 20% of annual planting. Broadleaves are considered to be important both because of their high-value timber and their environmental role. Implicit in these proposals is the expectation that the broadleaved timber will be of high quality and that whatever planning measures are needed to achieve this quality will be taken.

The need for planning is further emphasised in a message from the EU Commissioner: "Forestry by its nature requires long-term planning. Its multi-faceted nature and its interaction with the environment and with other areas of economic and social importance require furthermore that plans for the optimal development of forestry at national level ... be both comprehensive and integrated."

For broadleaves, in particular, long-term planning is also needed at local forest level, where every operation is considered in advance from crop establishment right through to the final harvest. Any undertaking that may span three or four generations of ownership and involves a number of different operations is worth thinking through. Furthermore, these operations are all closely inter-linked. Selection of a particular species will, within limits, decide the rotation length. Planting espacement will determine time of tending and thinning, and have an impact on the type and quality of stems available for selection. By and large, planting provides the platform for subsequent silvicultural management, and the thinning operation provides the opportunity for formative treatment of the crop. The effect of each action, or inaction, on the long-term quality of the stand is a feature that must be borne in mind.

The objective of high-value timber emphasises the need to produce high-quality broadleaved stands. High-value timber is invariably linked to quality in the tree. This is much more applicable in the case of broadleaves than in conifers. Quality in this context is defined in terms of large dimensions, absence of knots, straightness of stem, regular growth, and acceptable colour. These characteristics are largely conditioned by silvicultural management. The point is forcefully made in the Strategic Plan that "The quality potential of a forest is largely determined by the quality of its management." Managers, therefore, may need to re-focus on the silviculture of broadleaves, in terms of longer rotations, scale of operation, composition of mixtures and species characteristics.

2.2 GENERAL SILVICULTURAL STRATEGIES FOR BROADLEAVES

2.2.1 Growth characteristics of broadleaves and quality timber production

The silvicultural management of broadleaves is much more complex than for conifers. Conifers are relatively easy to grow and manage and, provided the basic principles of initial spacing, tending and timely thinning are applied, the desired end product can be achieved. Rotations are relatively short, at 35 - 45 years, compared with those of broadleaves, which range from 70 - 150 years.

Furthermore, site conditions for broadleaves will usually dictate that pure species stands will be small in area, and that they will grade into one another through artificial or natural means.

Broadleaves do not have the same degree of apical dominance as conifers. Given sufficient growing space the tendency is for broadleaves to produce large and heavy branches rather than stemwood volume. They are more prone to forking of the stem which, although it may be aesthetically pleasing, is of little commercial value. Silvicultural management aims to curb these tendencies and produce a product for which the timber trade will pay the highest price. Ideally, the trade requires straight tree boles 8 m or more in length, uniform ring widths, branch (and knot) free and dimensions of 40 cm diameter or more. The best sections of these stems should be suitable for veneer production and the remainder should be of a quality suitable for furniture manufacture. The objective is to produce the commodity that will maximise revenue and silvicultural management should be directed towards the achievement of this goal.

The response to growing space has more pronounced consequences for growth and quality in broadleaves than in conifers. Wide initial spacing or premature thinning will provide increased growing space for tree crowns but at the expense of stem quality; stem form disimproves, taper increases and live branches persist giving rise to knotty timber. In contrast, close initial spacing or late intervention improves stem form and taper: branches die earlier, remain small in diameter and are more readily shed when they die. This obviates the need for artificial pruning but sacrifices crown size and stem diameter increment.

The strategy for growing broadleaves, therefore, presents the forester with a silvicultural dilemma. To ensure stem quality and natural pruning broadleaves need to be grown in very dense stands. Yet, in order to provide the final crop trees with sufficient growing space to develop large crowns, as a prerequisite to the production of large diameter stems, stands have to be thinned early and heavily. The longer the stands are kept in a dense state, the smaller the stem diameter growth. This is especially a problem with pioneer species, such as ash, wild cherry and sycamore whose height growth and capacity for crown development culminate at a relatively early age.

The solution to the dilemma lies in a compromise:

- broadleaved stands should be kept dense until the branches have died on the lower part of the stem to a height of 6 - 10 m;

- when this state is achieved the potential final crop trees should be selected and released immediately from competition from aggressive neighbours; this release procedure must be repeated at frequent intervals to provide an opportunity for the final crop trees to develop their crowns.

2.2.2 Density at stand establishment

The strategy for the growing of quality broadleaves involves planting at a sufficiently high density to:

- restrict lateral branch (and hence knot) diameter development;
- encourage height rather than lateral growth;
- ensure that there is available at time of thinning an adequate number of potential final crop trees.

2.2.3 Pre-thinning treatment

During the pre-thinning stage the stand is, therefore, kept closely stocked to force upward growth of the leading shoot and control the lateral growth of side branches. Controlling the diameter growth of side branches is an essential element of broadleaved silviculture. Close stocking will ensure smaller lateral branches and easier shedding. In contrast to conifers, the ability of most broadleaves (except wild cherry) to shed branches naturally is an important element of broadleaved silviculture. However, large lateral branches will not die and be shed naturally for a considerable time. Their presence on the stem degrades timber quality.

Apart from wild cherry, artificial pruning (as opposed to formative shaping) of broadleaves should be undertaken only as a last resort. It is costly and must be repeated if long branch-free boles are to be obtained. It is not generally recommended as it leaves a pruning scar which, in slow growing species, will not occlude for many years thereby introducing avenues for fungal attack which may produce rot in the stem. If artificial pruning is necessary, it should be done before branch size exceeds 3 cm in diameter at the stem.

2.2.4 Tending and the selection of potential final crop trees

During the tending operation, when the crop is 5 - 8 m in height (earlier for light demanders than for shade bearers), potential final crop trees will be identified and favoured. The selection and removal of rough branched, malformed trees (wolves) in tending, is also an essential feature of broadleaved silviculture. These are usually dominants and co-dominants and are often competing with potential final crop trees. Only wolves and the occasional competing dominant should be removed in tending.

Sub-dominants and suppressed trees should be retained, even if they are badly formed.

2.2.5 Thinning

Thinning provides the silviculturist with the opportunity to mould the form and stem quality of the crop. How and when thinnings are done will have long-term consequences on the condition of the stand.

At thinning time (about 35 years for oak and beech but earlier for ash and sycamore) the stand quality will have been influenced by the following characteristics:

- high density stocking to ensure that the lateral branches are of small diameter;
- the death of these branches due to competition from surrounding trees;
- natural shedding of the lower branches;

- selection and removal of rough branched, crooked or malformed stems during the tending phase.

If good silvicultural practice has been followed the stand will contain a proportion of dominant trees of good stem quality which will now be selected as final crop trees. Attention is focused on these selected trees, to promote crown development and enhance their diameter growth. Trees competing with the selected trees are removed in thinning. The emphasis is on the continuing development of these trees. The main function of subsequent thinning treatments is to ensure that these selected trees are provided with adequate growing space. This silvicultural strategy will ensure the shortest rotation to achieve a stated diameter and the highest quality crop at the end of that rotation.

2.2.6   Final crop trees

The final crop trees represent an investment in the future stand. They are the trees that will remain at the end of the rotation and are consequently the main contributors to the value of the crop. Ideally they should be vigorous and healthy, with straight boles forging through the crown to the leading shoot, branch-free and with good symmetrical crowns. Trees which are not in the upper storey; those with forked stems, steep branching angle, spiral grain, damaged bark or those prone to epicormic branching, should not feature in the selection. The choice of final crop stems is crucial to the success of the crop. Once the selection is made it should not be changed without good reason. These stems should be checked in successive thinnings and in cases of emergency the necessary changes should be made in so far as that is silviculturally possible.

2.3   SILVICULTURAL PROCEDURES

The growing of quality broadleaves requires the implementation of a number of silvicultural operations which are common to most broadleaved species. These common elements are presented in the following sections.

2.3.1   Site preparation

2.3.1.1 *Fencing*

On most sites, regardless of method of regeneration, rabbit-proof fencing will be necessary. Care should be taken to bend the bottom 15 - 20 cm of netting wire outwards and cover it with earth to ensure that rabbits cannot burrow underneath.

Since fencing is costly some thought should be given to the shape of the area to be planted. A square shape will be most cost effective; long narrow rectangles are best avoided where possible.

2.3.1.2 *Vegetation control and soil preparation*

Competition from vegetation is a major problem at time of stand establishment. For both natural and artificial regeneration, growth performance will be greatly improved by planting into a vegetation-free soil. Research by Coillte, Teagasc and INRA (France) has shown that excellent results are obtained by pre-planting treatment of the vegetation with glyphosate. Its main purpose is to maximise water and nutrient supply to the plant but an added benefit accrues from the fact that exposed mineral soil is more efficient than vegetation in absorption of heat, thus providing conditions for improved root growth and overnight re-radiation. This may significantly reduce frost damage, an important consideration for frost tender species.

Land suitable for the establishment of broadleaves will be either:

- existing old broadleaved woodland in need of regeneration; or

- former agricultural land or coniferous woodland being converted to broadleaved woodland through afforestation/reforestation.

2.3.1.2.1 *Regeneration of old broadleaved woodland*

Regeneration of old woodland can be by artificial or by natural methods. Artificial regeneration is the norm in situations where it is intended to change species or where no suitable seed trees exist. In such situations the site is cleared of trees, other than those retained for shelter, and planted in the conventional manner.

In old broadleaved woodland the opportunity exists for either complete natural regeneration or a combination of natural and artificial methods. For natural regeneration to be successful soil preparation measures are necessary. The intensity of such measures will depend to some degree on the species being regenerated. Beech and oak need slightly more intensive soil preparation treatment than ash and sycamore but for all natural regeneration a vegetation-free seedbed is essential.

When the decision is made to regenerate a beech or oak stand by natural means, the forest floor is treated in summer with glyphosate to control weed growth. Then in the autumn the soil is rotovated twice, once before and once after seed fall.

- Rotovation before seed fall must expose the mineral soil. This is essential, especially on slightly acid soils, where conditions are not favourable to the breakdown of humus. In such conditions, a variety of bacteria and fungi attack and destroy seed during the winter period before germination - hence the need for cultivation to expose mineral soil and promote aeration.

- After seed fall a second rotovation is needed to reduce seed predation by animals and birds, and allow the seedlings to root in the mineral soil, thereby reducing losses through drought in spring.

Regeneration of ash and sycamore stands requires pre-treatment with herbicide, followed by one light rotovation prior to seed fall.

2.3.1.2.2 *Conversion of conifer woodland or agricultural land to broadleaved forest.*

Conversion of conifer forest to broadleaves generally involves clearfelling and reforestation. The establishment operations involved are essentially the same as afforestation of former tillage land or pasture.

Where a plough pan has developed on former tillage ground subsoiling will be needed. Pre-planting vegetation control with herbicide is recommended where necessary.

Former pasture needs no site preparation other than pre-planting treatment with herbicide to control grass and weeds. Excellent results are obtained by treating a 1 m wide strip with glyphosate. Strip ploughing, with overlapping ribbons, will provide for vegetation control and may reduce overall establishment costs. Such strip ploughing in combination with weed control may also influence the microclimate by improving the heat exchange between the soil and the air temperature near the ground.

Complete ploughing as a means of controlling vegetation is not recommended owing to the danger of subsequent invasion by noxious weeds.

2.3.2 Plant handling

Good plant handling procedures are necessary if serious losses are to be avoided. Care should be taken to ensure that roots do not dry out. Grading should not be done in the open. It takes time and increases exposure of roots to drying wind. The lifting operation in the nursery should be screened against drying wind if necessary. After lifting, plants should be placed promptly in specially designed storage bags, which are immediately sealed and opened only just before planting. The bags should be stored in a cool place, away from direct sunlight (which can cause overheating). Plants in transit should be treated gently and not thrown around unnecessarily.

Notch planting, with a T- or L-shaped slit, is suitable for broadleaves when plant size is small and it is done with care. Roots should be evenly distributed in the planting hole and the soil firmed-in, making sure to avoid bending of the roots or root collar. Cutting of roots, to make them more amenable to planting, should be avoided. With large plants, pit planting will often be necessary to ensure that the roots are not cramped in the planting position.

Where the soil and terrain permit the use of a planting machine will considerably reduce planting costs, particularly on large areas. Depending on the type of machine it may also provide better quality planting than its manual counterpart, in that the roots are allowed to hang vertically in the planting slit.

The ground should be vegetation-free, either through the use of herbicides or strip ploughing.

2.3.3 Spacing configuration

Practical experience has shown that, for a given stocking density, closer spacing within rows and wider distance between rows introduces a greater degree of competition than the equivalent square planting configuration. Thus, for a stocking density of 5,000 plants/ha, 2 x 1 m spacing is preferred to 1.4 x 1.4 m spacing as it induces greater competition between plants and gives better stem form. The wider distance between rows also allows for greater flexibility of movement within the stand at the tending and thinning stages. Furthermore, there is less walking distance, and a consequent reduction in cost, at the cultural stages of cleaning, shaping and tending.

2.3.4 Establishment of mixtures at planting time

Mixtures, intended to remain for the full rotation (as opposed to nurse mixtures), should be planted in groups of a minimum area of 100 m². On the premise that the number of final crop trees/ha will be 100, and therefore that each tree will occupy 100 m², this will ensure that at least one tree of the mixture species per group will remain in the final crop.

2.3.5 Vegetation management

As stated above (Section 2.3.1.2.2) pre-planting treatment of 1 m wide strips with glyphosate will reduce vegetation competition from grass and weeds in the first growing season. This should be followed by annual post-planting treatment to keep an area of 1 m² around the plant free of weed growth for a further 2 to 3 years. Treatment with herbicide should be undertaken with care and spraying of the plants should be avoided.

In situations where the vegetation is dominated by grasses, trampling is not considered to be a good method of weed control, since competition for moisture will not be affected by this procedure. Complete ploughing (if the site lends itself to this operation) as a method of pre-planting vegetation control (see Section 2.3.1.2.2) is effective for a year but subsequent invasion by noxious weeds makes it unattractive. Strip ploughing (two overlapping ribbons) or treatment with herbicide will usually produce the same effect at less cost.

2.3.6 Formative shaping

Broadleaves are much more prone to forking of the leading shoot than conifers. Close spacing encourages upward growth of the leading shoot, but in itself this may not be sufficient to provide the quota of select stems required for final crop trees. When the leading bud is damaged or killed, growth of lateral buds on the leading shoot then result in forking. Shaping improves the stem quality and enhances the opportunity for selection of good final crop trees.

Formative shaping is a silvicultural operation carried out in the early years to encourage the development of a straight stem. It is recommended where two or more leading shoots compete for dominance. The aim is to encourage forked or otherwise malformed stems to revert to a single leader.

The shaping operation should:

- be carried out in June - July;

- be confined to dominants and co-dominants;

- begin when the crop is 1 to 1.5 m tall;

- be repeated several times where forking is persistent, to provide straight boles, 6 m in length, on a quota of 1,000 potential final crop trees/ha (around 3 x 3 m) at the tending stage;

- be done with a hand secateurs up to a height of about 3 m, and with a long-handled secateurs at greater heights.

Competing shoots are cut as shown in Figure 2.1. Excessive branch removal should be avoided. Trees with badly deformed stems or those with coarse branching will normally be removed in tending. Shaping such trees should only be undertaken where there is an insufficient stocking of potential crop trees - otherwise the operation is wasteful of resources.

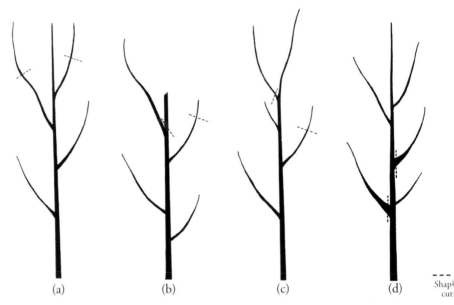

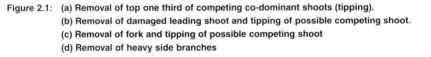

(a)   (b)   (c)   (d)   Shape cut

Figure 2.1: (a) Removal of top one third of competing co-dominant shoots (tipping).
           (b) Removal of damaged leading shoot and tipping of possible competing shoot.
           (c) Removal of fork and tipping of possible competing shoot
           (d) Removal of heavy side branches

Branches should be cut as in Figure 2.2 (according to the different branching patterns shown), as close to the stem as feasible, but avoiding the branch/bark ridge. Injury to the tree branch/bark ridge will facilitate the entry of rot organisms and ultimately reduce the timber value of the stem.

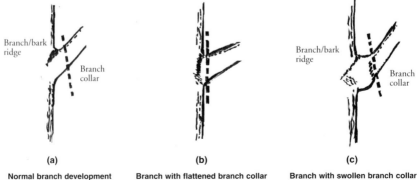

(a)   (b)   (c)

Normal branch development   Branch with flattened branch collar   Branch with swollen branch collar

Figure 2.2: Positioning of shaping (and pruning) cut in relation to bark/branch ridge

14

Formative shaping, by encouraging a single leading shoot, should ensure that 1,000 potential final crop tree candidates/ha will be available at the tending stage. From these candidates 100 - 150 final crop trees/ha, according to species, of good stem quality will be selected after the first thinning.

2.3.7 Tending

The aim of tending is to encourage the development of some 1,000 good dominants/ha as potential final crop trees. This is achieved by:

- removing coarse branched, forked and deformed stems (wolf trees);

- removing competing dominants, while at the same time retaining sufficient co- dominants as well as all sub-dominant and suppressed trees to promote natural pruning;

- controlling species such as willow and birch and other invasive species that are competing in the upper canopy.

The tending operation should take place when the crop is 5 - 8 m in height. It is required earlier for light demanders than for shade bearers.

The area in need of tending should be partitioned into sections by cutting racks (2 - 3 m wide) at 40 - 60 m intervals. Between these racks tending paths (1 - 2 m wide), spaced 6 - 10 m apart at right angles to the racks, complete the partitioning. The resulting rectangular network facilitates access to the crop, allows better organisation of work and quality of tending, and not least, leads to a reduction in costs. It is considered to be an essential element of the tending operation.

In planted crops the space between rows will serve as tending paths. For naturally regenerated crops, tending paths will need to be opened to provide access.

2.3.8 Pruning

The purpose of pruning is to produce knot-free, high quality timber.

For both naturally regenerated and planted crops the aim is to take advantage of the process of natural pruning by maintaining a sufficiently high stocking density up to a top height of 10 - 15 m (according to species). At this top height, tree boles should be free of live branches up to 6 - 10 m.

If artificial pruning is deemed necessary it should be confined to the 100 - 150 final crop trees/ha and done at the time of their selection. The feasible limit for artificial pruning is 6 m. Above this height the operation becomes too costly. As a general rule branches should not exceed 3 cm in diameter at time of pruning.

The pruning cut should be carried out as shown in Figure 2.2.

2.3.9   Thinning

The purpose of thinning is to redistribute the growth potential of the stand onto selected trees. It should improve the stem quality of the residual stand and provide adequate growing space for crown and stem diameter development of the selected trees.

The tending phase merges into the thinning stage when bole lengths, free of live branches for about 8 m, are achieved. Depending on species, first thinning takes place between 10 - 15 m top height.

The transition to the thinning stage is abrupt, and is characterised by a change in silvicultural strategy from negative to positive selection. Emphasis changes from removal of poor quality stems in tending (mainly wolves), to encouraging the development of the 1,000 potential final crop trees/ha (identified in tending) by providing them with adequate growing space. The improvement in growing space required for this development is achieved through crown thinning.

Crown thinning has a dual purpose:

- to encourage rapid diameter growth of selected trees and the production of the required diameters (40 - 60 cm at breast height) at the end of the rotation;
- to admit sufficient light to allow the survival of the sub-dominant and suppressed trees, which aid in the process of natural pruning and provide ground cover to control weed growth.

After the first thinning, and not later than 15 m top height, 100 - 150 final crop candidates/ha (preferably 8 - 10 m apart) should be selected from among the 1,000 dominants identified in tending. These should preferably be given a permanent marking to ensure that that they are not subsequently felled by mistake or damaged during extraction operations.

Subsequent thinning should take place at 1.5 - 3 m height growth intervals (depending on species) to favour the final crop trees by removing 2 - 3 competitors at each thinning. A normal thinning will reduce the number of dominants/co-dominants by about one third. The main rule in thinning is to ensure that the crowns of the final crop trees have sufficient growing space.

Sub-dominant and suppressed trees should be retained to prevent the development of epicormic branches and provide ground cover. Naturally regenerated wild cherry and other broadleaves should be retained where site conditions are favourable to their growth.

2.3.10   Underplanting

The main purpose of an understorey is to assist in natural pruning with consequent improvement in wood quality. Provision of an understorey will also control weed growth, increase stand volume production and give greater flexibility in management. The species most suitable for the purpose are hornbeam and beech.

Hornbeam, since it tolerates wetter soil conditions, may be considered more suitable than beech as an understorey on the heavy clay and gley soils. It has the added advantage that, because of its slower height growth and lower final height, it does not compete so aggressively later in the rotation. On that account it can be introduced either in mixture at planting time or later at the thinning stage.

Although hornbeam forms an essential component of broadleaved stands on the Continent, particularly naturally regenerated stands, there is little experience of this tree in Ireland. For that reason beech will usually be the preferred species until more information on hornbeam becomes available.

Planting beech in mixture with other broadleaved species at time of establishment is recommended only for shorter rotation (60 - 80 years) species. Beech is a highly aggressive species and, although it may be outgrown in the early stages of development, it tends to assume dominance midway through its rotation, at a time when an understorey is needed for longer rotation species. The preferred procedure is to underplant with beech after the first thinning.

The number of plants to be used in underplanting will be determined by management objectives. If the only intention is to create an understorey in order to curb the growth of epicormic branches, assist in natural pruning and provide ground cover, 600 to 800 beech/ha (or hornbeam), evenly distributed (4 x 3 m or 5 x 2.5 m), will be adequate. If this objective is extended to eventually develop the stand into a beech forest (after the principal species is felled), the density should be increased up to 1,600 beech/ha.

Plants 20 - 40 cm in height are adequate if there is no weed growth but if briars or other weeds are present plants 75 cm to 1 m in height will be necessary.

Although hornbeam and beech are excellent shade bearers they need some light to survive and develop, otherwise they will not be able to perform their intended role. Subsequent thinnings should cater for the development of the understorey.

2.3.11   Control of grey squirrel

The grey squirrel constitutes the most serious threat to the growing of broadleaves. All broadleaves, with the exception of wild cherry, suffer from damage to a greater or lesser extent. Apart from causing extensive damage to the branches this often leads to encirclement and death of the upper crown. Bark stripping damage can be severe if allowed to go unchecked. A number of methods are currently employed in the control of grey squirrel. Poisoning with warfarin is thought to be the most cost-effective method. Its use is legal, as the grey squirrel is not protected under the 1976 Wildlife Act. Special hoppers are available, which allow access to the bait by grey squirrels only. Use of warfarin is not recommended in areas still containing red squirrels.

Live trapping employs cage-traps usually adapted from mink traps. This method is relatively effective but can prove laborious; periods of pre-baiting and long trapping sessions are often needed.

Other methods employed involve shooting, alone or in combination with drey poking. The latter is much more effective than straight shooting but both are dubious as measures of damage prevention. Drey poking can only be effectively carried out while the trees are not in leaf in late winter and early spring and any impact made at these times is unlikely to have a lasting effect on numbers. Attempts to prevent damage to trees by killing squirrels in months other than April, May, June and July are considered to be largely a waste of effort.

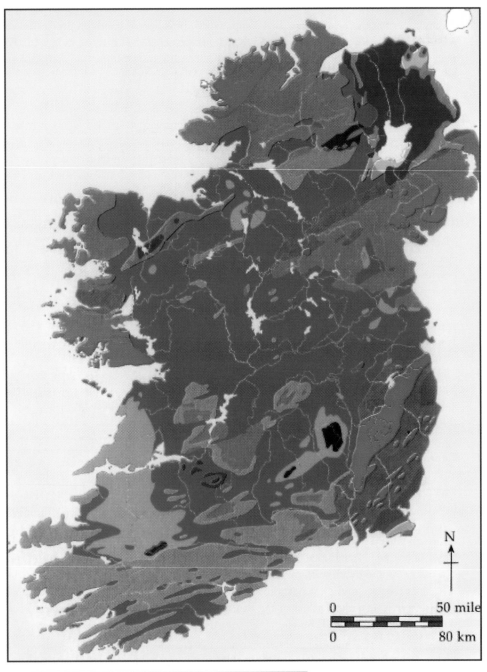

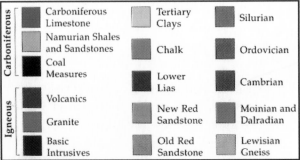

Carboniferous	Carboniferous Limestone	Tertiary Clays	Silurian
	Namurian Shales and Sandstones	Chalk	Ordovician
	Coal Measures	Lower Lias	Cambrian
Igneous	Volcanics	New Red Sandstone	Moinian and Dalradian
	Granite	Old Red Sandstone	Lewisian Gneiss
	Basic Intrusives		

Figure 3.1 Geological map of Ireland

3 Soils

3.1 SUMMARY OF OPTIMUM SITE/SOIL CONDITIONS FOR BROADLEAVED SPECIES

SITE/SOIL CONDITIONS SPECIES	ASH	BEECH	SYCAMORE	OAK
SITE DEMAND RANKING	1	2	3	4
ELEVATION/REGION	Lowlands	Lowlands	Lowlands & sheltered uplands	Lowlands & sheltered uplands
FROST	Intolerant	Intolerant	Tolerant	Moderately tolerant
DRAINAGE	Continually moist, but well-drained	Periodically dry, well-drained	Moist, well-drained	Sessile: well-drained Pedunculate: less well-drained
FERTILITY	High	High <=> Medium	High <=> Medium	Sessile: Medium Pedunculate: Medium <=> High
SOIL REACTION (pH)	Topsoil: > pH 5.0 Subsoil-Parent material: about pH 7.0	pH 6.0 - 7.5	pH 4.5 - 8.2	Sessile: pH 4.0 - 6.5 Pedunculate: pH 4.5 - 7.5
BEST SOILS	Brown earths & grey brown podzolics, preferably deep; tolerates moderate gleying, also acid topsoil provided pH increases with depth	As for ash, but slightly drier & preferably calcareous throughout the profile	Brown earths, grey brown podzolics, rendzinas, acid brown earths, brown podzolics	Acid brown earths, brown podzolics, podzols & gleyed variants of these for pedunculate
BEST REGIONS	Midlands, north Leinster, east Connaught, north Munster	As for ash	As for ash and beech	South-east Leinster, south Munster, south-east Ulster

3.2 INTRODUCTION

Guidelines on site suitability for the main broadleaved species are available, mainly from Britain. The practitioner, however, often finds them too general and somewhat impractical on a local scale. This applies particularly in Ireland, which has a varied and complex soil distribution.

The site suitability guidelines are based on a limited survey of growth performance and stem quality of the four species distributed throughout the country (Appendix). Soils information was collected from a representative sample of the survey plots (Table 3.2). The prime consideration for inclusion of sample sites was that they should contribute information on the range of site types on which the species were growing.

Species	Number of plots	
	Growth performance survey	Soil study
Ash	39	15
Beech	80	22
Oak	56	25
Sycamore	17	6
TOTAL	192	68

In the soil study, a soil pit was dug in the middle of the selected stand. The soil was described by examination of the soil profile, noting characteristics of the soil horizons. A soil sample was taken from each horizon and brought to the Coillte Site Studies Laboratory at Newtownmountkennedy for analysis of pH and free calcium level. The on-site soil description and the results of the laboratory soil testing enabled each soil to be identified and classified, such as brown earth or grey brown podzolic.

The site suitability requirements of the individual species are derived from a combination (1) of applying the experiences gained, as well as the results, from the soil study, and (2) of the widely known general site suitability guidelines referred to.

When considering the suitability of sites and soils for most broadleaved species, particularly those for which an economic return is expected, it is convenient to categorise areas into uplands and lowlands. The uplands of Ireland are generally unfavourable for successful broadleaf growth, due mainly to poor climatic conditions and a preponderance of the poorer soil types (whose development are promoted by the poor climatic conditions).

The lowlands are clearly where the focus should be in any drive for broadleaf expansion. Therefore, in the sections that follow emphasis will be placed on those lowland soil types where successful broadleaf growth is most expected. However, the other soil types will also be dealt with in order to:

1. understand the differing circumstances which cause their formation, so as to appreciate the context for the existing distribution of soils in the country;

2. describe the different soil types so that the grower can identify them, and be enabled to make a well-based decision on whether broadleaf production is possible on a given soil and, if so, what species?

3.3   SOIL FORMATION AND DISTRIBUTION IN IRELAND

3.3.1   General

The type of soil produced at any location, in Ireland or anywhere else in the world, is determined by the relative influence of the five factors of soil formation, that is, parent material, climate, topography, living organisms (plants and animals), and time. A feature of the soils in Ireland is the overwhelming influence that parent material and climate have had (and continue to have) on their formation and development.

The importance of parent material as a soil-forming factor in this country is due to the varied deposits left behind by the many glacial episodes that occurred in Ireland's recent geological history. This is in contrast to other parts of the world where glacial activity was absent or at least substantially less. In such areas the parent material may extend for large stretches with little differentiation, resulting in relatively uniform soils produced, such as those formed from loess material (windblown silt and sand) and distributed over immense areas of Europe, Asia, and North America.

The importance of climate as a soil forming factor in Ireland is due primarily to the rainfall component. The scope for varying influences by this factor is great, since there is a wide variation in annual rainfall distribution, ranging from over 3,000 mm in the west to less than 750 mm in the east, a remarkably wide variation in such a small country.

The rest of this section will elaborate on the role of the major soil-limiting factors in Ireland, that is, parent material, climate (rainfall), and topography.

3.3.2   Parent Material

A feature of Irish soils is their extreme variability, which often makes soil classification and surveying on a local scale quite difficult. The variability is due to the fact that most soils in Ireland have been developed from deposits left behind by one or more glaciations. The advance and retreat of the glaciers meant that the underlying rocks were crushed, transported, and ultimately deposited as so-called drift material, which is the source (parent material) from which soils develop.

The type of drift material left behind can vary enormously, both chemically and physically. The chemical characteristics of the drift deposit will depend largely on the nature of the rocks (ranging from acid to calcareous) over which the glaciers travelled. The physical characteristics will have been influenced primarily by the source of the material (for example marine or non-marine), how it was deposited (for example sorted or unsorted), and by the extent to which pressure was applied to it (leading to impeded drainage). Since Ireland was affected by at least two glaciations, each involving several advance and retreat phases, it can be appreciated that the scope for differences in deposits (parent materials) which give rise to soils is great.

In spite of the complexities noted some broad generalisations can be made:

1.   In many areas the drift deposit is a reflection of the bedrock directly underlying it. For example, the widespread limestone drift occurring in the general midlands region of the country coincides closely with the extent of the limestone bedrock (see Figure 3.1). Most soils suitable for broadleaved species occur in this category (that is, soils derived from limestone drift), comprising the brown earth and grey brown podzolic Great Soil Groups. However, many of the soils within the limestone drift category can also have severe limitations for tree growth, the main ones being excessive levels of carbonate and impervious materials, both of which inhibit root growth.

2.   The mixed limestone-sandstone-shale drifts in the valleys of the southern part of the country are generally derived from the underlying limestone rocks together with sandstone/shale eroded from the surrounding hills. These soils are generally very suitable for broadleaf growth, since the soils have favourable levels of fertility (conferred by the limestone) and ideal drainage (conferred by the mixture of drift materials of

varying texture). The Great Soil Groups occurring in this category will depend largely on the composition of the drift mix in the parent material. Thus, where limestone predominates then brown earth and grey brown podzolic soils (alkaline soils) will occur, but where sandstone/shale predominates then acid brown earth and brown podzolic soils (acid soils) will tend to prevail.

3.3.3   Climate

Climate, more specifically rainfall, can be as important as parent material as a factor in soil formation in Ireland and sometimes even more so. The influence of rainfall lies in its capacity to remove, as it percolates down through the soil (through a process called leaching), nutrients and other elements from the upper to the lower soil layers. In extreme cases, nutrients can be removed from the soil altogether. As the intensity of leaching increases so too does the degree of soil infertility.

Since rainfall is generally greater in elevated regions there is a tendency for upland soils to be more leached, and thus more infertile, than lowland soils. (This is compounded by the generally thinner soils and poorer parent materials in most of the upland areas of Ireland.) The uplands, therefore, are covered mostly by soil types in which leaching is a dominant process; such soils include the following soil types: podzols, iron pan soils, and brown podzolics of low base status. Where water movement is restricted, due for example to a flat or concave topography, then peat will accumulate at the top of the soil, giving peaty variants of podzols and ironpan soils.

Lowland areas, in contrast, are comprised mainly of soil types where leaching is a relatively minor process in soil formation, because of the lower rainfall in such areas. Brown earths, grey brown podzolics and brown podzolics of medium-high base status are the principal soil types occurring in the lowlands.

3.3.4   Topography

The main influence of topography is in its effect on the distribution of water or materials transported by water: (i) runoff water, (ii) soil moisture content, (iii) depth to water table, and (iv) eroded materials. The nature and extent of the topographic effects determines the type of soil produced. For instance, flat areas commonly bear soils of poor drainage (for example, peats and gleys), due to a tendency for receiving water as runoff from higher ground and from which there is little or no runoff. This is in contrast to steep-moderate slopes, where a propensity to runoff is typical, a factor that facilitates free-draining soils (for example, podzols and brown podzolics). Dramatic illustrations of the importance of topography as a soil-forming factor abound in Ireland. For example, drumlins, although small in area, often contain a logical pattern of very contrasting soil types. A typical case is the sequence of soil types from top to bottom of the drumlin: (a) gleys on the poorly drained flat drumlin top, (b) brown podzolics and brown earths on the free-draining drumlin mid-slopes, and (c) gleys, peaty gleys, and peats on the poorly drained drumlin footslopes.

3.4.1 Method for describing and identifying soils

Soils are produced from the interaction of soil processes, such as physical and chemical weathering of parent material, leaching, podzolisation, and gleying. A wide variety of different soils is possible, depending on the contribution of these soil processes, particularly as the processes themselves are controlled by the factors of soil formation mentioned previously in Section 3.3, that is, parent material, climate, topography, organic matter, and time.

A given set of soil process interactions produces a soil with a characteristic profile, usually with layers or horizons aligned roughly parallel to the soil surface. Soils can be described and identified through examination of the characteristics of the soil horizons, such as depth, colour, texture, and organic matter content.

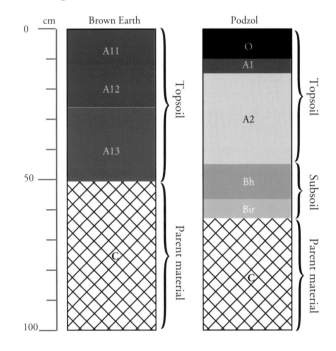

A common method of identifying or classifying soils uses the O, A, B and C system of naming soil horizons. The following is a brief explanation of what each of these so-called 'master horizons' represent:

O horizons - contain more than 20% organic matter; present in podzols, peaty podzols, and peaty gleys.

A horizons - represent the 'topsoil'; upper mineral horizons which are brownish in colour due to presence of plant/animal remains; lower part of A horizon can be pale in colour due to loss of iron and humus through leaching and podzolisation.

B horizons - represent the 'subsoil'; lower mineral horizons between topsoil (A) and parent material (C); colours usually different from A and C horizons, the colours being darker through accumulation of iron/humus removed from the overlying A horizon.

C horizons - represent the 'parent material' from which the A and B horizons have developed, that is the loose, unconsolidated material from the upper portion of the bedrock or glacial drift; less developed than the A and B horizons, resulting in a paler and more poorly structured horizon.

The above are called master horizons, since several sub-divisions of them are possible. For example, the A master horizon may be divided into A1 and A2 sub-horizons, the A1 representing a mix of organic and mineral materials, whilst the A2 represents a layer which has been subject to loss of humus and/or iron, leaving it paler in colour than the A1. Even the horizon sub-divisions themselves may be sub-divided in certain circumstances, such as illustrated in the brown earth diagram, where the A1 has been sub-divided into A11, A12 and A13, primarily on the basis of colour differences.

3.4.2   Major soils in Ireland

The following major soils are described: brown earths, podzols, brown podzolics, grey brown podzolics, rendzinas, gleys, and peaty variants of some of these soils.

Blanket peats and *Sphagnum* peats are excluded as it is assumed that these soils are readily identifiable and would not be planted with broadleaved species for commercial production. Other soils, such as podzols and gleys (some of which would be dubious in terms of suitability for commercial broadleaf production), which are not so readily recognised, are described so that some basis is provided for deciding which variants of them are suitable/unsuitable for broadleaf planting.

3.4.2.1   *Brown Earths*

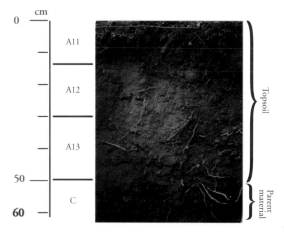

Figure 3.1: Brown Earth

These are free-draining, loamy mineral soils, which have no obvious horizons in the typical profile, a B horizon often being absent. The uniformly brownish-coloured profile is due to the fact that leaching is minimal, since brown earths are generally found in the low-rainfall lowlands. Furthermore, their parent materials are at least reasonably endowed with bases (calcium, magnesium, and potassium), their parent materials are readily broken down (weathering), and weathering is intense enough to release sufficient bases to largely compensate for those lost through the leaching process.

Brown earths may be acid or alkaline, depending on the base status of the parent material, acid brown earths having a lower base status than alkaline brown earths. Where impedance to drainage exists brown earths will tend to develop gley characteristics in the impeded zone.

3.4.2.2 *Rendzinas*

Figure 3.2: Rendzina

Rendzinas are extremely shallow calcareous soils (usually not deeper than about 40 cm) over limestone bedrock, which is frequently exposed at the surface. They often occur in small pockets in association with shallow brown earths, lithosols (shallow stony soils, nearly devoid of organic matter), and outcropping rock. Rendzinas are quite similar to shallow brown earths, the only distinguishing feature being a darker A horizon in the rendzina, due to a higher organic matter content. Rendzinas, and shallow brown earths, have a restricted localised distribution, the rendzinas confined mainly to north Clare (Burren), and the shallow brown earths occurring in the mid-western areas characterised by limestone bedrock at shallow depths.

3.4.2.3 *Podzols*

Figure 3.3: Podzol

Podzols are developed from acid parent materials. They are strongly acid, coarse-textured soils (sandy side of 'loam') so that drainage is very free. They occur on the uplands, and high rainfall on such areas means that leaching is a dominant process in their formation. Leaching removes soluble nutrients, and when sufficiently acid (acidity increases as nutrients are removed), iron and aluminium are also removed from the A horizon. This leaves a pale, leached A2 horizon and various possibilities for B horizon sub-divisions, depending on the material(s) deposited by podzolisation from the A horizon. Thus, if both humus and iron are leached to the B, the presence and location of the humus is signified by the designation Bh, and that of iron by Bir.

The upper part of the B horizon has a black or very dark brown colour, the lower part being merely brownish in colour, due to having less humus.

Where leaching is extreme the upper part of the B horizon may be somewhat compact or even cemented into an iron pan (a thin 2 - 3 mm, usually continuous layer of iron oxide), which can be a restriction to rooting. If cementation develops to the extent that it restricts downward movement of water then gley characteristics will be evident above the cemented layer. In such situations peat will tend to accumulate at the surface, giving rise to a peaty podzol, where the peat is 20-40 cm deep.

3.4.2.4   Brown Podzolics

These are milder versions of the podzols. They are well drained, but less intensively leached soils than the podzols. A feature of the typical brown podzolic soil profile is a surface A1 horizon, which is thicker and has a more intimate mix of organic and mineral material than in the A1 horizon of the podzol. A leached A2 horizon may be present but, if it is present, it will be faint. A red-brown B horizon underlies the A horizon, the colour reflecting the (moderate) leaching of iron compounds from the A horizon, but there is no iron pan, or even cemented layer. Brown podzolics are usually found on mid-slope locations and, because of their favourable physical and chemical characteristics, they are normally ideal broadleaf soils.

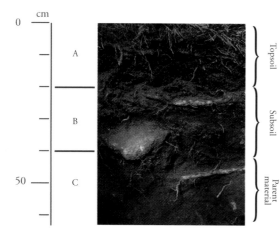

Figure 3.4: Brown Podzolic

3.4.2.5   Grey Brown Podzolics

In contrast to the podzols and brown podzolics, the grey brown podzolics are developed from calcareous parent materials. The importance of this fact is that the high lime content renders it chemically impossible for the removal of iron and aluminium compounds to occur within the soil. What does happen is that clay is translocated from the A2 to the B2 horizon, so that the latter has a much heavier texture than that of the overlying A horizons. Grey brown podzolics are important broadleaf soils because of their many favourable characteristics, particularly their high pH and medium or high base status and their free-draining nature.

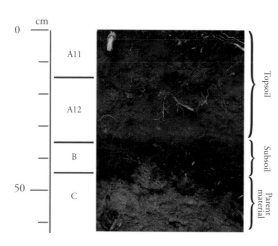

Figure 3.5: Grey Brown Podzolic

3.4.2.6 *Gleys*

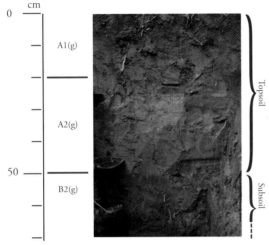

cm
0

A1(g)

A2(g)

50

B2(g)

Topsoil

Subsoil

Figure 3.6: Gley

Poor drainage in gleys is due to waterlogging, the duration of waterlogging varying from periodic to permanent. The waterlogging can arise for several reasons: (1) drainage restricted by an impervious parent material, due to a high content of clay, or by an impermeable compacted layer (both cases are surface-water gleys), and (2) drainage restricted by a high water table which overlies an impervious layer beneath the C horizon (ground-water gleys).

Surface-water gleys are more extensive than ground-water gleys. Ground-water gleys are less dependent on rainwater for their formation; they tend to occur on a more local scale, and primarily in the lowlands where conditions for their development (a high water table) are more likely to happen, for example, unbroken (impermeable) bedrock and alluvial river-basin situations.

In spite of their different modes of origin, both types of gley have common features in their soil profiles. Because of the lack of aeration in the soil the profile will have a grey appearance, and blue to blue-grey where more permanent waterlogging exists. In less waterlogged conditions, or where there is a fluctuating water-table, the upper mineral horizons will be aerated to some extent in local spots, such as in old root channels or soil cracks. Aeration of these local spots changes their colour from grey to brown or red-brown, giving the affected areas of the soil profile a mottled appearance. A broad generalisation can be made that the more mottled a gley soil is - in terms of abundance and depth of occurrence in the soil profile - the more suitable the soil is likely to be for tree growth.

3.4.2.7   *Peaty Gleys*

Figure 3.6:Peaty Gley

Peaty gleys have peat depths up to 45 cm (soils with peat depths exceeding 45 cm (in the undrained condition) are classified as deep peats). The upper mineral layer of the peaty gley is pale grey, and the subsoil is mottled pale grey and yellow as in the surface-water gley, although the mottled high-clay subsoil may be absent in the shallower versions of the peaty gleys.

3.4.2.8   *Podzolised Gleys*

Figure 3.6: Podzolised Gley

Another gley of some considerable importance in Ireland is the podzolised gley, which is an intergrade soil between the podzol and surface-water gley. The podzolised gley therefore has features of both soil types, that is leaching or removal of substances (podzol) from the topsoil, and water impedance. In contrast to surface-water gleys and peaty gleys, which tend to occur on soils derived from fertile parent materials with high silt and clay contents, podzolised gleys generally are derived from infertile parent materials with high sand content. Podzolised gleys are extensive in the old red sandstone regions of the south and south-west. Peat up to 20 cm thick is sometimes present at the surface, but this may often be absent due to removal in the past for use as fuel. Beneath the peat layer is a greyish mineral layer (substances leached out), which gradually merges with a brownish layer showing numerous rusty-coloured mottles (substances accumulated from above). Podzolised gleys generally have sandy loam to sandy clay loam textures and are usually stony near the surface. These soils occur wherever drainage is impeded but most commonly on the middle slopes of hills (podzols, with or without iron pan, generally develop at higher elevations, whilst gleys of the surface-water and peaty gley type occur more frequently on flat areas and lower slopes).

Ash

Fraxinus excelsior L.
Fuinseog

Ash,
Donadea,
Co. Kildare.

4.1 Summary

Ash is currently the most sought after commercial broadleaved tree in Ireland. It is the only species suitable for making hurleys and also provides valuable material for the manufacture of furniture. For both of these purposes it should be grown rapidly. Slower grown material can be suitable for veneer if it is knot-free, of regular growth and has a diameter greater than 50 cm.

Ash is the most demanding of the broadleaves in regard to site and needs a deep, moist, free draining, fertile soil, of about pH 6-7, for optimum growth conditions. It is rarely found in large stands and will benefit from the shelter provided by other broadleaves species. It is very light demanding and will require heavy thinning throughout its life to attain the desired rate of diameter growth. It has a relatively short economic rotation, 60 - 80 years. After this age the wood tends to become discoloured with consequent depreciation in value.

On suitable sites ash will be the first choice for the private grower. If such sites are not available it is probably better to grow some species other than ash.

4.1.1　Key characteristics

- Strong light demander, except when very young
- Very site specific
- Susceptible to damage by late spring frost
- Very responsive to vegetation control
- Susceptible to summer moisture deficits
- Susceptible to forking of leader
- Good ability for natural pruning
- Prolific seed producer
- Immune (almost) to damage by grey squirrel

4.1.2　General silvicultural treatment

Top height m	Stocking after treatment trees/ha	Comment
0.4-0.9	3,300	Planted at 2.0 x 1.5 m / (2 m between rows).
2 - 3	3,000	Formative shaping - singling of forked leaders.
4 - 5	3,000	2nd formative shaping (if necessary).
7 - 8	2,100	Tending - remove wolves, deformed and cankered stems.
10	1,000	Heavy crown thinning - underplant with beech or hornbeam.
12 - 13	700	Crown thinning of competing dominants.
15	490	Select 150 final crop trees/ha; thin to remove competitors.
17 - 18	340	Thin to remove competitors to final crop stems and to release beech/hornbeam understorey. Thinnings are suitable for hurleys.
18 - 27		Thin at intervals of 2 - 3 m height growth to remove competitors to final crop stems.
27 - 28	100 - 120	Fell final crop at about 50 cm diameter breast height.

4.2　NATURAL DISTRIBUTION AND OCCURRENCE

Ash has a wide natural distribution, with climates as markedly different as oceanic and continental. It is found growing both at low elevations and in mountain regions. On very rich and well-drained sites it can form the dominant species but on drier and on fissured limestone sites it will be found mainly in mixtures. It is a component of the higher parts of the riverine forest together with oak and elm.

Ash is indigenous throughout Europe from the Mediterranean as far north as central Sweden and from the Atlantic to central Russia (Figure 4.1). It extends eastwards through northern Turkey to the Caspian Sea and is also found in North Africa. Unlike oak and beech, it is rarely found in pure stands of any extent. More usually it forms a component of broadleaved mixtures.

It is native to Ireland where, in the Celtic Laws of Neighbourhood, it was listed among the noble trees, ranking even above oak.

Figure 4.1: Natural distribution of ash

The facility with which ash regenerates naturally from seed ensures that it is one of the most common trees of the countryside and is the main tree species in hedgerows. In most broad-leaved woodlands ash will be found regenerating in small openings where it forms dense thickets. Yet, despite this capacity for regeneration, the number of good quality ash stands in the production stage is extremely few. This may be partly due to the high demand for hurley ash material but it is also undoubtedly a reflection of the general unsuitability of previously acquired state forest land for ash production.

Ash regenerates freely on most soils in Ireland but shows good growth only on fertile soils with sufficient rooting depth. In state forests, stand composition varies from pure ash to mixtures with Norway spruce or broadleaves but stand size is almost invariably small.

Inventory data indicate an area of almost 2,300 ha of ash (13 % of all broadleaves), either pure or in mixture, in state forests.

A sample survey of such stands shows ash growing well in mixture with beech on limestone derived soils in Athenry (Kilcornan) and Portumna forests. On thin soils over fissured limestone in Galway and Clare pure ash stands show stunted growth but single trees of naturally regenerated ash in beech stands on these sites are growing successfully. Its potential on good old red sandstone sites is evident in a small stand in Clonmel forest (Curtiswood). On drumlin slopes in Swanlinbar forest a number of stands have been harvested for hurley material and at Gosford forest in Northern Ireland an excellent stand is growing on a gleyed brown earth. The poorest growth of ash is in the Wicklow - Wexford area. In Shillelagh forest, renowned for quality oak, the growth of ash is poor and in Coolgreaney forest (Barnadown) ash growing on heavy gley soil is stagnating.

4.3   PROVENANCE

Ash is a native species that occurs abundantly throughout Ireland. Its abundance, fecundity and ability to remain viable in storage for up to 6 -7 years has resulted in home collected seed being used widely in the planting programme. Until the beginning of the 1990s only 5% of the seed sown was imported and most of that is attributable to one purchase of 225 kg from Denmark. Local provenance variation in ash is not known at this stage nor is the performance of UK or continental sources when grown in Ireland.

As a general rule, seed source studies have shown that when dealing with native species local provenances tend to out-perform those from different latitudes and climates. Thousands of years of evolution have adapted native species to the often unique ecological conditions of a region. Planting local origins should therefore be the desired option. This is particularly so with ash since selective fellings would not have had an impact on the genetic constitution of the species as a result of the abundance and resilience of its natural regeneration and its ability to coppice.

Seed production of ash in closed stands is generally poor (due to lack of thinning which results in small crowns). Therefore, collections have almost exclusively been made from hedgerow trees; and it is likely that these will continue to be the main seed source until seed stands are brought into production. For the longer term, a seed orchard has been established by Coillte with grafted material from trees intensively selected in plantations for good growth and form.

The necessity to import seed and plants of ash should be considerably less than for the large-seeded species of oak and beech. If imports are necessary then registered British and Dutch sources are recommended.

4.4   ECOLOGICAL DEMANDS AND CHARACTERISTICS OF THE SPECIES

4.4.1   Biology, autecology and growth performance

4.4.1.1   *Biology*

As the *excelsior* in its scientific name suggests, the common ash is one of the most magnificent trees of Europe, reaching heights of more than 40 m at its maximum although 30 m is more the norm. Like most of the 60 ash species of the world, it has buds set in opposite pairs and pinnately compound leaves.

Ash has a light crown, generally with steeply angled branches when young. Even as a solitary tree it never reaches a crown diameter comparable with beech.

Its root system is wide-spreading and consists of a taproot and long side roots, which provide stability against storms.

Flowering is in April; panicles of flowers develop from side buds before the leaves flush. The flowers are wind pollinated, partly monoecious (one individual carrying both sexes), partly dioecious. Female trees tend to grow more slowly. Fructification starts relatively early (at around 30 years) but solitary trees may bear fruit much earlier. Mast years are usually every 2 - 3 years.

Ash seeds ripen on the tree during the period July to October. They are shed over the winter and early spring, but do not germinate until the following spring. Ash seedlings should therefore not be expected to appear for eighteen months. However, if the seeds are collected as soon as they fill (before ripening), and are sown immediately, a high proportion will germinate in the following spring.

4.4.1.2 *Seed storage and treatment*

For nursery plant production the seeds are harvested when they turn brown in October/ November. The moisture content can be quite high at this stage, so the seeds are spread out in a thin layer to dry and turned regularly to avoid heating. When the moisture content has been reduced sufficiently the seeds are stored in a cool shed until the following June.

Ash seeds, when ripe, are practically incapable of germinating if no treatment is applied before sowing. This pre-treatment (stratification) procedure consists of the following steps:

* in June after collection, mix the seeds with equal parts of moistened sand and peat in outdoor pits;

* turn the mixture regularly (once every ten days) and re-moisten if necessary;

* maintain the seed at an ambient temperature of 15 - 20°C for 6 - 16 weeks to allow development of the embryo;

* winter chilling (a minimum of 16 weeks at 3°C) is needed to break embryonic dormancy;

* check seeds regularly during January, February and March to ascertain if germination has commenced.

The seed can be sown from mid-March onwards.

Ash seed can be stored in the dry state for up to 10 years. The weight of 1,000 ash seeds varies from 65 - 100 g.

4.4.1.3 *Autecology*

Although ash is classed as a strong light demander it will tolerate considerable shade in youth but will stagnate if not released within a few years. It is therefore often classified as a pioneer species although it can also be regarded as a climax species on riverine forest sites.

Ash needs overhead space and light for the development of a large crown to attain rapid growth of the stem. Although the planting of ash in pure crops on bare land provides adequate light and avoids the risk of competition from nurse species, it presents a danger from frost.

Ash is susceptible to damage by late spring and early autumn frosts. In late mild autumns it sometimes fails to complete hardening-off of its leading shoots before the sudden onset of winter. This can result in the death of buds and upper parts of the young branches and lead to forking of the shoots in the following year.

Late frost in spring may kill the opening buds or emerging leaves, as ash is extremely sensitive to late spring frost. This also leads to forking.

Ash is the latest of the broadleaved species to flush: its strategy obviously is to avoid frost damage by this behaviour.

Planting ash with a nurse species does not necessarily overcome frost problems in low-lying situations; such areas should therefore be avoided.

4.4.1.4   *Growth performance*

Like other pioneer species ash shows very rapid growth in the early years. Current annual height growth culminates around 20 years of age, with an average annual height increment of 50 - 60 cm. It diminishes to 25 cm around the age of 50 and to 8 - 9 cm at 100 years of age. This is in contrast to the growth of beech, which culminates later and is more sustained (Figure 4.2).

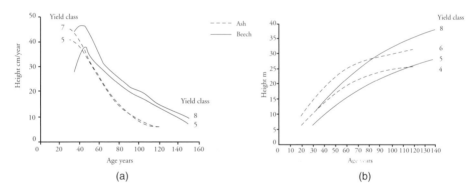

Figure 4.2: Current annual height growth (a) for ash (Volquardts, 1958) and beech (Schober, 1967); and height-age graph (b) for ash (Volquardts, 1958) and beech (Schober, 1967)

In the German models[1], current annual volume increment for ash culminates at 40 - 50 years of age, compared with beech which culminates later and is sustained for a longer period (Figure 4.3 a). Cumulative volume production for ash is comparatively low (Figure 4.3 b).

[1] See Glossary for definitions of British and German yield classes

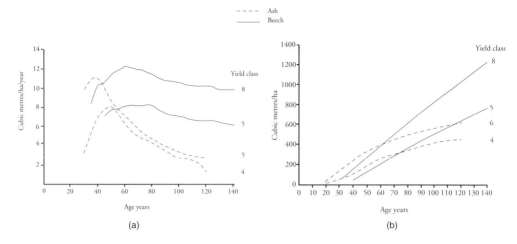

Figure 4.3: Current (a) and cumulative (b) volume increment of ash and beech in Germany ((a) from Volquardts, 1958 and (b) from Schober, 1967)

The British sycamore/ash/birch/ composite yield models (currently under revision) show a maximum yield class of 10. In terms of height/age this is intermediate between the best two site classes in Northern France (*Nord-Picardie*) up to 40 years of age. Thereafter, the French models show much more rapid height growth and at 80 years have dominant heights of 34 and 30 m compared to 26 m for the British model.

The rapid early growth easily enables ash to outgrow competing ground vegetation. Ash, however, is susceptible to competition from grasses up to late in the rotation. This is particularly so on drier sites and is obviously due to water deficiency and also to competition for nutrients induced by the grasses.

4.4.2   Site requirements

Ash is so site demanding that it accommodates very little room for error in terms of site selection. This means that it is most unlikely to achieve optimum growth unless it is grown on continuously moist, fertile soils. These soils should be in the lowlands, and in areas that are frost-free.

Compared to beech, sycamore and oak, ash has a high demand for nutrients, particularly nitrogen and phosphorus. To service this demand the soil has not only to be relatively high in nutrient levels, but also moist enough throughout the growing season to facilitate water-mediated transport of nutrients to the tree roots.

The ideal ash site is to be found primarily amongst the soils developed on limestone parent materials (see Figure 3.1), namely the brown earths and grey brown podzolics.

These are to be found mainly in the central area of the country, covering an area roughly encompassed by the counties Louth, Roscommon, Galway (east of Lough Corrib), Tipperary, Kilkenny, Carlow, Kildare, and Meath.

Good ash can be found amongst the rendzinas and shallow brown earths of the north Clare (Burren) and mid-Galway regions. However, these areas tend to be very small, restricted to deeper pockets within the overall matrix of soils. Extreme care needs to be taken in selecting a site for ash in these areas due to the danger of the soils becoming too dry. An ash mixture with beech and/or sycamore may be prudent on such sites; the ratios of the species mix being determined by soil depth, with ash favoured for the deeper soils.

Suitable ash sites can also be found in the Munster old red sandstone valleys, primarily in north Munster, such as in Curtiswood Property, Clonmel Forest. These occur in those parts of the valleys - in or around the valley bottoms or footslopes - which have a significant component of limestone and/or shale glacial material in their soil parent material. The fine texture of the limestone and/or shale glacial material confers a clay-loam texture, thus allowing the soil to be water-retentive in dry spells. In addition, the limestone and/or shale material enables the soil to have reasonably high pH and nutrient levels for ash.

Ash has a wide tolerance for pH in the topsoil, which should not be less than pH 5.0, but it should approximate neutrality (pH 7.0) in the lower parts of the soil profile.

Results from the soil study show that the brown podzolics and acid brown earths, covering large parts of Wicklow and Wexford, present problems for ash growth, although they are excellent for other tree species. Several factors may be involved: (1) low pH, (2) low base status, (3) excessive drainage (prone to drought), and (4) low phosphorus availability in the soil.

As regards the low phosphorus availability problem, it is a paradox that there is often no shortage of phosphorus in these soils. However, the relevant soils have an intrinsic chemical capacity to fix or lock up the phosphorus, so that it is unavailable to the tree.

Laboratory tests on ash foliage from a Shillelagh (Co Wicklow) brown podzolic site bear this out, the analysis showing a severe phosphorus deficiency, as well as a severe deficiency of nitrogen and a marginal level of potassium. It is not surprising therefore that all crops, agricultural as well as forest, readily respond to fertilisation on such soils, particularly phosphorus fertiliser. However, phosphorus fertilisation of these soils may not be sufficient for ash, because of the other potentially limiting factors mentioned (low pH, low base status, and excessive drainage).

A more striking and direct indication of the potential problem of phosphorus availability was shown for a second poor ash stand in Shillelagh. The soil is more fertile than the previous site, which is manifested by the luxurious levels of nitrogen and potassium in the ash foliage; nonetheless, the phosphorus levels were sub-optimal.

For good growth ash needs soil conditions found only in the lowlands, although it will survive at higher elevations and tolerate exposure. It regenerates freely on a variety of sites ranging from wet to dry, but the presence of regeneration should not lead one to assume that such sites are suited to the growing of ash. Although ash can be grown successfully on soils with a pH as low as 5 it develops best on deep, moist, free-draining and fertile soils of about pH 7. Such sites are not widely available for planting. Attempting to grow quality ash on other sites is not likely to be successful, because high quality ash needs to be grown rapidly. It is probably better not to grow ash if this cannot be reasonably assured.

Ash benefits from a good supply of water in the soil but it will not tolerate stagnant water conditions, swampy or compacted soils. Sites should be moist with a movement of water through the soil.

4.4.3 Post establishment factors affecting growth and development

As a forest tree ash is relatively free of insect pests or fungi. However, it is liable to suffer damage to its leading shoot and this, more often than in continental countries, leads to serious forking.

4.4.3.1 *Abiotic factors*

Because of its wide spreading root system ash shows a high degree of stability and is rarely windthrown.

However, late spring frost, especially when unusually late, may kill the buds and newly flushed shoots, resulting in forking of the leader.

It has been shown that death of opening buds of seedlings will occur after 18 hours exposure at - 3°C. Early autumn frost may lead to the same result.

4.4.3.2 *Biotic factors*

Ash is prone to damage by hares and rabbits if left unprotected. Rabbit damage can take the form of gnawing of the bark, while hares prefer to snip off the stems.

Deer (fallow, red and sika) tend to browse intensively on young plants and should be excluded, usually by fencing. Otherwise, seedlings and saplings will be destroyed. Large deer populations may destroy seedlings and saplings and may lead to heavy bark stripping of pole stage crops up to 20 cm diameter.

Unlike other broadleaves, such as sycamore, beech and to a lesser extent oak, damage to ash by grey squirrel is rare.

Ash has few pests and diseases apart from the ash bud moth (*Prays fraxinellus*), which is also regarded as being one of the main causes of forking. It tends to be more of a problem on larger areas of pure ash.

Stem canker is caused by the bacterium *Pseudomonas savastanoi* or by the fungus *Nectria galligena*. It appears as a dark brown corky swelling on the stem.

Timber properties

Ash is a markedly ring porous wood. Viewed in cross section the very large earlywood (springwood) pores of the annual ring are easily discernible, alternating with the strong, hard, dense latewood (summerwood). This latter feature gives ash its toughness after drying. Air-dried ash timber weighs 700 - 800 kg/m³.

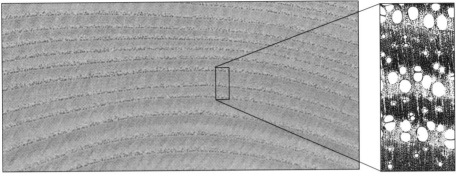

Cross section of ash   **X 40**

Slow grown ash timber tends to be brittle and breaks easily. The more rapid the growth, the greater the proportion of latewood and the better its flexibility and bending ability. Rapidly grown timber is therefore very suitable for sports goods such as hurleys, hockey sticks and for tool handles where shock resistance and strength are required. For uses that require a handgrip, its smooth surface which rarely splinters, is a valuable quality.

Ash is a popular timber for furniture because of its strength, clean white appearance and varied surface figure. It lends itself readily to steaming and bending without breaking or losing strength. This process is used to form curved parts of furniture and the ends of hockey sticks.

Regular and large annual rings are necessary to produce good quality wood and a ring width of 4 - 5 mm (0.8 - 1 cm annual diameter growth) is required for quality sawlog material. This growth rate also leads to excellent machining properties for furniture production. Smaller ring widths give wood of lesser strength which can be used for veneer, while larger ring widths give even better mechanical properties favourable to products which require greater strength, flexibility and elasticity.

Like all ring porous woods (for example oak and sweet chestnut) irregularities in ring width depress the quality and give rise to tension in the wood during the kiln drying process. Variations in ring width result from irregularities in thinning cycles, with alternating periods of stand competition and release. A large increment in diameter consistent with good quality wood is difficult to achieve without regular and consistent heavy thinnings.

In the tree, the mechanical attributes of ash wood remain stable up to about 60 years of age after which they tend to diminish. At 70 to 80 years of age the rapid diameter growth rate begins to decline and the onset of black (or brown) heart usually appears, giving a black or brown discolouration at the heart of the tree. Although its cause is unknown it is variously attributed to factors of site, origin of tree and age. Ash grown on wet or swampy ground is said to be more prone to black heart, as is ash originating from coppice origin.

Black heart has very little effect on the mechanical properties of the wood but it usually depreciates the merchantable value for sports goods. In France, the presence of more than 20% discolouration at the heart of the tree at stump level leads to a reduction in value of the order of 50% but in Ireland it is often regarded as a novel feature by craft workers for cabinet making. Globally, however, the fashion trend is for white timbers.

In trees not affected by black heart there is little colour distinction between heartwood and sapwood: the general colour is white. The wood is non-durable and perishable if exposed out-of-doors. The heartwood is moderately resistant to preservatives but the sapwood is more permeable.

4.5   PRODUCTION GOALS

Production objectives for ash include material for the manufacture of hurleys as well as logs for the production of sawtimber and veneer for the furniture industry. Hurley material should preferably be 28 - 32 cm diameter for optimal conversion. High quality timber logs should be 50 - 60 cm diameter at breast height.

4.5.1   Growing ash for hurleys

The Forest Service Inventory (1973) estimated that there were 5,500 ha of ash in private ownership but much of it was regarded as overmature for hurley manufacture. In state forests the area of ash is currently almost 2,300 ha, equivalent to 13% of the total area under broadleaves. Although it is much younger than the ash in private ownership, its quality is thought to fall short of the optimum for hurley material.

The national game of hurling will continue to be a major outlet for good quality ash. Specifications for hurley ash require a straight butt length of 1.5 m, free of branches or defects such as extraction damage or other injury. Ideally, the tree will have four equally spaced well-developed buttresses and a diameter at breast height of 28 - 32 cm. Only the butt length with buttresses is used for hurleys: the remainder of the stem is unsuitable. The demanding specification and current scarcity has resulted in premium prices for quality ash butts.

The very attractive price for hurley material ($£350/m^3$) has been a great incentive for afforestation with ash. It is, however, important to take into account that this applies only to the butt volume of approximately 0.1 m^3 (assuming a length of 1.5 m and diameter of 30 cm). For the enterprise to be profitable the remainder of the stem (with the greater volume) should also be of sufficiently high quality to command a high price.

Currently, the main use for ash in Ireland is in the manufacture of hurleys and this is expected to continue for the foreseeable future. Attempts to address future supply and demand for ash led to an extensive study by the Forest Service in the 1980s.

This estimated that almost half a million hurleys of all sizes are used each year. Based on this figure and assuming average production from good quality butts, it was calculated that an area of about 50 ha/annum would be sufficient to supply the hurley ash market. The study assumed that hurley ash can be produced on a 25 years rotation, so the total area of ash needed for hurley production was estimated to be about 1,250 ha.

Even allowing for a less optimistic rotation of 40 years, which is more in keeping with the requirements of stems of 30 cm diameter breast height, hurley requirements can be supplied from some 2,000 ha of a normal age class distribution, grown purposely for hurleys. This takes no account of thinnings suitable for hurleys produced under other regimes.

In the light of this study, and taking account of current afforestation with ash, it seems reasonable to assume that production objectives should be directed towards much broader product requirements, such as sawlog and veneer. These will include hurley ash material in the form of thinnings.

4.5.2 Production of high quality timber

Outside the specific market of hurley material the primary objective should be the production of logs for veneer and sawtimber with regular and large annual rings (4 - 5 mm in width radially). Boles should be 50 - 60 cm diameter at breast height and be cylindrical and branch-free. If the stated diameter growth rate can be achieved (0.8 - 1 cm), this objective will be realised over a rotation of 60 - 80 years. A secondary objective will be the production of hurley material from thinnings (28 - 32 cm diameter).

The common dimensions required for sawing are logs with a minimum length of 2.5 m and a mid diameter of 26 cm upwards. The silviculturist will therefore seek a branch - free bole of a minimum length of 6 m, preferably 8 m, with a diameter at breast height of 50 - 60 cm. A breast height diameter increment of 1 cm/year will be adequate for this purpose; diameter growth should not fall below 0.6 cm/year if quality timber is required.

4.6 STAND ESTABLISHMENT

4.6.1 Site preparation

4.6.1.1 *Fencing (see Section 2.3.1.1)*

4.6.1.2 *Vegetation control and soil preparation (see Section 2.3.1.2)*

4.6.2 Regeneration of old woodland

4.6.2.1 *Utilisation of naturally regenerated ash groups*

Ash shows a remarkable capacity for regeneration on many soils, even on those where it will not grow well, such as heavy gleys and on dry thin soils overlying limestone (see Section 4.4.2).

In Central Europe input of nitrogen from atmospheric pollution has improved the humus status on all sites resulting in conditions for better germination, especially for ash and sycamore. This has led to a remarkable increase in the spread of young ash growth in many places.

In woodland settings a small number of mother trees well distributed throughout the stand and a receptive seed bed often are the only prerequisites needed for natural regeneration of ash (see Section 2.3.1.2.1). The emerging young growth occupy openings in the canopy, caused by windthrow or other factors, where there is sufficient light for it to survive.

On suitable old woodland sites, therefore, natural regeneration offers a simple and inexpensive approach to stand establishment, coupled with an opportunity to protect the seedlings against frost in the early years. For the rapid development of the seedlings sufficient overhead light is always necessary. Partially closed canopies have to be opened up and small gaps need to be enlarged to more than 400 m² in area to give the light demanding ash plants a chance to grow. Normally, seedlings already established will win the race against grasses, bracken or briars before the latter begin to proliferate.

4.6.2.2 *Planned natural regeneration of ash*

Where the regeneration process has not already begun but is being sought, proactive measures will often be necessary to assist in this purpose. For ash, the group shelterwood system shown in Figures 4.4a and 4.4b offers the best approach for success.

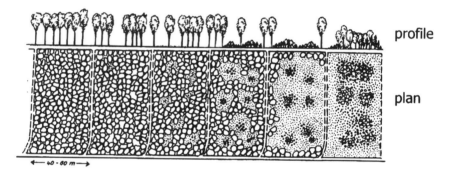

Figure 4.4a Schematic representation of the group shelterwood system (from Burschel and Huss, 1997)

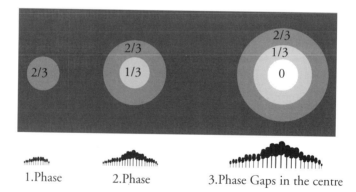

Figure 4.4b Group shelterwood system; group enlargement and spatial development over time (1/3 of the original stocking is removed at each intervention)

The group shelterwood system consists of the following phases:

- The canopy will be slightly opened up over a roughly circular area about 30 m in diameter (average height of a final crop tree) to provide just sufficient light for ash seedlings to become established without encouraging the development of weeds. Depending on the size of the stand, further groups circular in outline, about 60 m apart may be laid out, starting at the eastern edge and moving in a westward direction (opposite to the prevailing wind direction).

- Shortly after the seedlings have appeared in the first established groups the canopy should be further reduced in these groups and the potential regeneration area enlarged by slightly opening up the stand around the groups. Further groups may be established to the west of the existing groups.

- The remainder of the canopy in the original groups will be finally removed and the reduction in number of mature trees will be continued in a circular band around the now fully opened gap.

- Some further groups will be established, and the existing groups will be gradually opened up as mentioned before.

Progress of the operation depends mainly on the light demands of the species concerned. With ash, for instance, it may take only 5 years until the canopy is fully removed in each group and may need 10 - 20 years to regenerate a whole stand, depending on its size. The system provides a great deal of flexibility, as progress in the removal of the canopy can be perfectly adapted to the development of the young trees. Where less light demanding species are involved it may be much slower. Moreover, different species could be regenerated in groups beside each other by varying the rate of opening of the canopy.

In situations where the soil is not receptive, because weeds or mor (acid humus) formation impede natural regeneration, rotovation treatment (see Section 2.3.1.2.1) should be carried out. In practice, seedlings will often have already appeared in parts of the stand and can be accepted. In other parts they are absent, and because of adverse conditions, it may not be advisable to wait any longer. Therefore, soil treatment usually needs to be carried out only on smaller parts of a stand.

Seventy-year old ash stand, Val St. Pierre, France. Ideal stand and site conditions to commence natural regeneration

4.6.2.3   *Artificial regeneration*

On suitable sites where seed bearers in the canopy are absent it may be opportune to plant ash beneath the shelter of the existing canopy. Depending on the structure of the stand and silvicultural targets with regard of mixtures, this can be done groupwise or on the whole area, either in one operation at once or in consecutive years.

Because of the favourable effects of the overstorey on the establishment of the young plants and their growth during the early years, the plant density can be slightly reduced compared with spacing recommendations for afforestation (see Section 4.6.3).

4.6.2.4 *Combination of natural and artificial regeneration*

For cost effective silviculture of broadleaves, foresters should adopt a more pragmatic approach towards natural and artificial regeneration when dealing with old woodland. This involves abandoning the rigid dogma of mutually exclusive regeneration systems which has prevailed through decades of afforestation. Nature's bounty should be accepted where it is presented, and modified, if necessary, to suit the situation. Today many foresters are prepared to combine both natural and artificial regeneration systems in accordance with conditions in the field.

It is now more acceptable to use groups of naturally regenerated plants, and fill-in or enrich by planting those areas where regeneration has not occurred. Nursery plants can be used for this purpose but often it is more expeditious to use wildings from adjacent areas or neighbouring stands.

The combination of both regeneration methods, using patches of natural regeneration combined with enrichment plantings, is especially appropriate for the establishment of mixtures. Apart from ecological advantages it has the potential to save a lot of money. However, it needs a much more intensive approach to the investigation and planning of silvicultural operations than that which prevails under the clearfell and replant regime.

4.6.3 Afforestation

Good ash sites are almost exclusively former tillage or pasture. Where a plough pan has developed on former tillage ground subsoiling will be needed. Former pasture needs no site preparation other than pre-planting treatment with herbicide to control grass and weeds (see Section 2.3.1.2).

Plants normally used are 1+1 and 1+2 years old transplants. Age and quality recommendations regarding these are shown in Table 4.1.

Ash (foreground) oak and beech, riverine forest of the Danube. The ash is 130 years old and has a top height of 43 m

44

Table 4.1: Recommended sizes for bare-rooted ash transplants

Organisation	Maximum age years	Minimum root collar diameter mm	Maximum root collar diameter mm	Minimum height cm	Maximum height cm
Forest Service	3	7	-	40	75
	4	12	-	60	90
British Standards Institute	-	5	9.5	20	50

For plant handling procedures refer to Section 2.3.2

4.6.3.1   *Pure ash stands*

Extensive stands of pure ash are rare. Ash occurs almost invariably mixed with other species, either in intimate mixture or in pure groups limited in area. The specific site requirements of ash will usually limit the size of area on which pure ash can be successfully grown. Furthermore, large monocultures tend to be more prone to attack by ash bud moth and have the leaders broken by wind.

Afforestation of former agriculture land meets the high light demand for this species but presents problems, which can only be obviated by shelter. This is especially so in frost hollows in the Midlands and other low lying situations where the emerging leaves and buds may be severely damaged by late frosts. Such areas should be avoided for pure ash planting.

For rapid growth ash requires side shelter. This can be provided by topographic features or, where this is absent, by wood edge shelter of other species. On sites open to exposure pure ash should be intermixed in blocks, of around 500 m², with groups of other species, such as sycamore or a suitable conifer, which will provide side shelter.

Pure ash should be planted in rows 2.0 m apart and 1.5 m in the row (3,300 plants/ha).

4.6.3.2   *Ash mixtures with other broadleaves*

Good ash sites are so limited in extent that ash should be the first option as the main species on such sites. The other main broadleaved species, beech, oak and sycamore are much more accommodating in regard to site, although the subsequent silvicultural treatment may be more difficult. In mixtures with ash these broadleaves can have either a serving and subsidiary role or form a permanent part of the mixture.

The functions of the serving species are:

- to assist in natural pruning and enable the ash to produce the desired quality timber;

- to provide ground cover and, at the end of the rotation, produce suitable conditions for natural regeneration, if required.

The main serving species are beech and hornbeam (see Section 2.3.10).

Beech, oak and sycamore can form permanent mixture components of ash stands. Sycamore rotations are similar to those for ash but this can be extended to much longer rotations without deterioration of timber quality, if desired. Beech and oak both have rotations that are much longer. They will be outgrown by the ash in the early stages and the light demanding oak may suffer from suppression. At the end of the ash rotation (60 - 80 years) the beech will begin to assume dominance over oak and sycamore. Therefore, the purpose of intimate mixtures, containing a number of broadleaved species, should be given some thought at time of establishment. If it is intended that a species, other than beech, will form a component of the final crop, it is best to arrange mixtures in groups of, at least 100 m (crown area of one final crop tree). This will provide the flexibility needed to control the composition of the final crop.

In beech and oak stands occasional ash stems and other species like wild cherry, especially those originating from natural regeneration, should be accepted as a minor component.

In former times elm was the natural companion of ash on moist soils of high nutrient status. Unfortunately it is no longer a contender for a mixture role because of Dutch elm disease.

4.6.3.3 *Ash mixtures with conifers*

Mixtures of ash with conifers require that the purpose of such mixtures be defined so that the appropriate management can be applied. Many authors recommend mixtures for the purpose of providing side shelter on exposed sites, listing European or hybrid larch as a suitable species for this purpose. Larch and ash have much in common in that they are both strong light demanders; they grow rapidly on suitable sites and because of their light foliage they are unable to dominate the site. In band mixtures (maximum 3 lines alternating), a more fundamental problem may arise in that the larch may compete with or even dominate the ash during the first decade, in which case the larch may have to be sacrificed if a quality ash crop is desired. Greater freedom of management, a similar side shelter and more environmentally pleasing effect is obtained by planting in small groups, chequer-board fashion, with a group size as mentioned above.

Both ash and larch will benefit from the introduction of an understorey at a later stage (see Section 2.3.10).

Norway spruce and ash in alternating bands has been a common mixture in state forests where the ash has been intended for removal for hurley material. However, subsequent maintenance of the mixture has proved difficult in that it does not provide the growing space necessary for good ash growth without a grade of thinning unsuited to the spruce. It is therefore not recommended.

4.6.4 Vegetation management

As already mentioned (Section 2.3.1.2) competition from grass and weeds is a major problem in all young stands of ash. Vegetation management (see Section 2.3.5) is therefore an essential operation and should be carried out until the plants are no longer threatened by competition from the vegetation. Ash will benefit from this operation until the plants are at least 2 m in height.

4.7   FORMATIVE SHAPING

Ash has better apical dominance than beech and oak but damage to the terminal bud by frost and insect larvae result in forking of the leading shoot. In such circumstances formative shaping is necessary (see Section 2.3.6).

4.8   TENDING

In ash stands established by natural regeneration it is recommended that the first tending operation should take place when the crop reaches a top height of 5 m, at which height the coarse branched, deformed and cankered trees are removed. This is followed by a second intervention at a top height of 7 - 8 m, when the same procedure is repeated. At this stage naturally regenerated compatible species such as wild cherry, sycamore, beech and oak are favoured to encourage species diversity. In ash crops planted at 3,300 plants/ha one tending operation at 7 - 8 m top height will suffice (see Section 2.3.7).

For both naturally regenerated and planted crops the objective should be to maintain a sufficiently high stocking density up to a top height of 10 m, thereby taking advantage of the tendency for ash to prune itself naturally.

4.9   PRUNING

Ash is one of the best broadleaves for natural pruning. At the recommended initial stocking density of 3,300 plants/ha natural pruning should provide for branch-free boles to the required height of 6 - 10 m on the designated 150 trees/ha. If natural pruning is judged to be insufficient supplementary artificial pruning should be undertaken (see Section 2.3.8). This is preferable to waiting for natural pruning to take place by delaying thinning and retarding diameter growth.

In plantations of heterogeneous or lower stocking densities artificial pruning may be essential to obtain a branch-free bole of a minimum length of 6 m. This should be done in two stages. The first stage involves the selection and pruning (to 2.5 - 3 m) of the 200 best trees/ha at a top height of 8 - 10 m.

The second stage will involve a further pruning (to 6 m) of 150 of these selected stems/ha at a top height of about 15 m. These will be the designated final crop trees. At both stages pruning should maintain a living crown whose length corresponds approximately to half the total height of the tree.

4.10   THINNING

For ash, the tending phase merges with the beginning of the thinning stage at a top height of 10 m. At this height the process of natural pruning is deliberately slowed down by a heavy crown thinning, in order to promote the development of a large crown and stimulate diameter growth (see Section 2.3.9).

Two thinning schedules for ash, based on stem numbers/ha and rate of height growth, are presented in Table 4.2. Thinning begins at 10 m and is repeated for every 2 or 3 m increase in top height, according to site fertility. For optimal sites and very fast growing ash, the thinning cycle is based on a 3 m increase in height growth. Sites of medium to good quality are thinned for every 2 m of top height increment.

Table 4.2: Thinning schedules for ash on very good/good and medium sites

SITE			
Very good/good		**Medium**	
Top height m	**Stocking after treatment trees/ha**	**Top height m**	**Stocking after treatment trees/ha**
0.4- 0.9	3,300	0.4- 0.9	3,300
7 - 8	2,100	7 - 8	2,100
10	1,000	10	1,000
13	680	12	720
15	460	14	520
18	310	16	375
21	210	18	270
24	145	20	195
27	100	22	140
30	Fell	24	100
		26	Fell

The schedules are modelled to an extent on recommendations based on French research in naturally regenerated stands in *Nord-Picardie*. Features in common with the French model include tending at a height of 7 - 8 m, a substantial reduction in stem numbers at the first thinning (10 m top height) and selection of final crop trees at about 15 m top height. The substantial reduction in stem numbers at the first thinning is deemed to be essential to allow ash to develop its crown at this stage. Tree numbers/ha after the second and subsequent thinnings are however, much greater than in the French model and conform more closely to 'main crop after thinning' stem numbers, for the given top heights, in British yield models. Thinning intensity, in term of stem numbers, is 32% for very good/good sites and 28% for medium sites.

Selection of final crop trees is made at top heights of about 15 m. For both site classes it is recommended that 150 final crop stems/ha should be identified at this stage. They will be mainly dominants, with straight boles free of live branches to 6 - 10 m height and large well-developed crowns. From this stage onwards thinnings are made to favour these potential final crop stems and to remove diseased trees.

These thinning schedules aim to produce trees of 30 cm mean diameter at breast height at 40 years (top height 20 - 21 m) for hurleys, and of 40 - 50 cm diameter breast height at 60 years of age for commercial timber.

Time of first thinning is largely dictated by the need to develop a large crown at an early age in order to stimulate diameter increment. Delaying thinning (beyond 10 m top height) will give a longer branch-free bole but will retard crown and diameter development. Unlike other broadleaves ash relies heavily on height growth to develop its crown and will respond slowly if allowed to suffer from competition. It needs to be kept growing vigorously. A substantial reduction in stem numbers at 10 m top height caters for this. Subsequent thinnings are much more gradual.

Selection of 150 final crop stems at about 15 m top height allows the forester to focus on the final crop at an early stage and promote the development of these stems. Crown size is the key. The trees should at all times have sufficient growing space to avoid contact of the crowns even in high winds.

To summarise:

- wolves, deformed and cankered stems are removed in early tending;
- a relatively high stocking density is maintained in pure ash stands (both naturally regenerated and planted) up to a top height of 10 m to encourage natural pruning;
- a substantial reduction in stem numbers (from 2,100 to 1,000 trees/ha) occurs at 10 m top height to encourage crown development;
- selection of potential final crop trees is made at about 15 m top height for all site classes.

4.11   UNDERPLANTING

Pure ash stands have a low volume production/ha, suffer from weed competition throughout the rotation and have a slight tendency to develop epicormic branches. Therefore, shade-bearing species should be introduced to form an understorey (see Section 2.2.10).

Sycamore

Acer pseudoplatanus L.
Seiceamar

Sycamore,
Ravensdale,
Co Louth

5.1 Summary

Although sycamore is a common species in hedgerows and shelterbelts, stands of sycamore are relatively rare in Irish forestry. From the small number of stands that exist, however, there is sufficient evidence that the species can play a significant role in afforestation. On rotations up to 100 years it is thought to be more productive than ash or beech. Unlike those species its wood does not suffer from discolouration over long rotations. The timber is used in the furniture trade and is highly prized as veneer.

Sycamore accommodates itself to a wide range of site conditions and grows well on calcareous soils and on non-calcareous topsoils with an increasing pH with depth. It will not tolerate stagnant water conditions; day-long flooding, particularly in summer, usually leads to deterioration in growth and in wood quality and may even lead to the death of the trees. It prefers a cool and humid climate and is relatively tolerant of late spring frost.

The major threats to sycamore are from the grey squirrel and deer. Damage can be serious if control measures are not applied.

5.1.1   Key characteristics

- Tolerant of shade in youth but light demanding later
- Prefers cool, humid sites
- Tolerant of late spring frost
- Responsive to vegetation control
- Susceptible to forking
- Moderate natural pruning ability
- Prolific seed producer
- Very susceptible to damage by grey squirrel

5.1.2   General silvicultural treatment

Top height m	Stocking after treatment trees/ha	Comment
0.4- 0.75	4,000	Planted at 2 x 1.25 m. (2 m between rows)
2 - 3	3,500	Formative shaping - singling of forked leaders.
4 - 5	3,500	2nd formative shaping (if necessary).
7 - 8	2,200	Tending - remove wolves and deformed stems; in sycamore/larch mixtures remove competing larch.
12 - 14	1,000	Heavy crown thinning - option to underplant with beech or hornbeam.
15	650	Select 150 final crop trees; thin to remove competitors.
17 - 18	400	Thin to remove competitors to final crop stems and to release beech/hornbeam understorey.
18 - 27		Thin at intervals of 2 - 3 m height growth to remove competitors to final crop stems.
27 - 30	100 - 120	Fell final crop at 40 - 60 cm breast height diameter.

5.2   NATURAL DISTRIBUTION AND OCCURRENCE

Sycamore is native to central and southern Europe where it occurs in mountainous regions from the Pyrenees to northern France and eastwards to the Black Sea. It is a typical tree of the mountains and reaches its optimum in the Alps at an altitude of 700 - 1,000 m (see Figure 5.1). Sycamore follows beech, with which it is normally found in mixture. It is fully naturalised in the Netherlands, northern Germany, Denmark and southern Sweden, to which it has been introduced by man. It may have been brought to Britain by the Romans or introduced as late as the 16th century. Like ash it is rarely found in pure stands of any extent; more usually it forms a component of broadleaved woodland.

Figure 5.1: Natural distribution of sycamore

Sycamore was first recorded in Ireland in 1632, but it was probably introduced at an earlier date. It was planted originally as a mixture in shelterbelts and along avenues on estates but around 1700 planting in blocks began. In the early decades of the 18th century sycamore wood was among those allowed in the making of barrels for the export of meat, butter, tallow and fish, which suggests that there was a substantial supply available. By the end of the century Samuel Hayes recorded a sycamore near Rathdrum, Co Wicklow "at two miles from that town on the road to Shillela" which was "15 feet in circumference" (145 cm diameter), "with the most beautiful head in proportion; this was the largest sycamore I ever saw".

Today, sycamore is a common species in shelterbelts on farms and in hedgerows. It is tolerant of exposure to wind and salt spray, as is evidenced by its survival and growth along the Atlantic seaboard.

Sycamore stands are relatively rare in Irish forestry. Considering its invasiveness this is surprising and must be due to the perception among foresters that it is a weed species. Yet, among the number of stands surveyed there is sufficient evidence that the species can have a significant role to play in forestry.

In state forests, inventory shows an area of slightly less than 300 ha of sycamore as the dominant species, equivalent to 2% of broadleaved woodland. Ages range from the beginning of this century up to the 1960s, with one stand originating in 1890.

A sample survey of these stands shows that the species can accommodate a wide range of site conditions.

Most of the stands are small, and some are of coppice origin, but the stands in Dundalk, Monaghan, Ballinasloe (Co Galway), Callan (Co Kilkenny), Kilsheelan (Co Tipperary) and Mullinavat (Co Kilkenny) help to demonstrate the potential of the species on suitable sites. Apart from stands in Newmarket (on gley) and Kilsheelan, which suffer from some forking, all show very good stem form. It also grows well in mixture with ash (Ballygar Forest, Co Galway) and with beech (Portlaoise Forest, Co Laois).

5.3   PROVENANCE

Like beech, sycamore is an introduced species, which has become successfully naturalised in Ireland. As a non-native species of continental origin it is possible that the present naturalised seed origin may not be the best for this country. Little is known of seed source variation in this species. Provenance trials have not been established to date in this country but are planned.

Like ash, sycamore is a prolific and regular seeder and seed can be stored for up to 6-7 years without loss of viability.

Home collections have therefore been the main supply of seed for the greater part of this century. While more productive sources than the naturalised origin may exist, the fine quality of home grown stands would suggest that this source is suitable and should be a first choice in the absence of definitive provenance test data. If imports are necessary then Dutch, northern German, British and northern French sources are possible alternatives.

5.4   ECOLOGICAL DEMANDS AND CHARACTERISTICS OF THE SPECIES

5.4.1   Biology, autecology and growth performance

5.4.1.1   *Biology and tree form*

Sycamore is one of Europe's most impressive broadleaved species, reaching a height of 35 m in stands. Isolated trees develop widely spreading domed crowns. Its longevity is comparable with the oaks and trees of 300 - 500 years of age are known in central Europe. During its vegetative phase, growth is monopodial but this can change to sympodial as flowers develop at the leading buds. The timing and intensity of flowering is reported to have a dramatic impact on tree form which results from the forking induced every time a shoot flowers.

Its roots show an intensively twisted heart shaped system, with marked vertical development. Sycamore is therefore very wind firm and, on this account, is frequently compared to the oaks in terms of stability.

Like all *Acer* species its buds are set in opposite pairs. Its leaves resemble those of the true sycamore (*Platanus* spp.), from which it derives its name. They have five lobes, cut halfway to the base and are acute and coarsely toothed.

Flowering is in April - May, simultaneously with unfolding of the leaves. The flowers are insect pollinated. Isolated trees start to flower at 15 - 25 years of age but trees in stands rarely flower before the age of 30 years.

5.4.1.2   *Seed storage and treatment*

Seed is produced annually and is generally adequate in terms of quantity. Ripening takes place in September/October and dispersal follows within a short period.

For nursery plant production, collection of seed takes place during these months when the samaras change from green to yellow in colour. Moisture content at this stage is of the order of 42 - 55%. For over-winter storage drying is not necessary but for longer storage (2 - 3 years) the moisture content should be reduced to 24 - 32% (for the whole samara) or 30 - 42% for the seed only.

Pre-treatment with a stratification medium of equal amounts of moist peat and sand is carried out in pits during early February. This process takes about 4 - 5 weeks until 5 - 10% of the seeds begin to germinate. If sowing is not possible at this time the seeds, including the medium, can be stored at - 3°C for up to three months without any loss of viability.

Pre-treatment without a medium involves placing the seed in mesh sacks in water for 24 hours and then transferring them to unsealed plastic bags and storing at 3°C. The seeds are mixed once a week to ensure that they are kept uniformly moist. This pre-treatment lasts for 4 - 5 weeks.

Seeds can be sown in autumn after collection without any pre-treatment but frequently these germinate too early in spring and suffer frost damage.

The weight of 1000 winged seeds varies from 70 - 180 g.

5.4.1.3 *Autecology*

Sycamore does best in a cool and humid maritime climate. It is relatively tolerant of late spring frosts and is not susceptible to damage by early autumn frost.

Sycamore demands a continuous supply of moisture for good growth. In this regard high atmospheric humidity, or sites with good water storage capacity, can compensate for low precipitation. Young sycamore is susceptible to competition from grasses for moisture and this may result in complete failure of plantations. Like ash, older stands also suffer from competition from grass sward.

In Denmark, the best production of sycamore is in coastal regions. In central Jütland, with a slightly more continental climate, growth rates are markedly reduced.

In terms of shade tolerance sycamore is regarded as an intermediate species, tolerating a considerable amount of shade in its youth, much more than ash and almost as much as beech. At a height of 1 m, however, it has largely lost this tolerance. At this height sycamore growing in shade tends to fork and bend towards the source of light. From the pole stage onwards its demand for light greatly increases. It can therefore be deduced that, although sycamore can be established under shelter (for example in shelterwood systems), it will attain optimum development only in full light conditions.

In recent decades, sycamore is regenerating much more freely in European forests than it did before. Many foresters attribute this to more intensive thinning in recent times. Others argue that it might be the result of improved topsoil conditions due to nitrogen input from atmospheric pollution.

5.4.1.4 *Growth performance*

Over the first 30 years sycamore shows excellent growth performance on suitable sites. After this period growth tends to decline and beyond 50 years of age it falls off considerably.

There is a paucity of data on continuous measurements of sycamore experimental plots. Nevertheless, some yield models have been developed from existing stands in Britain, Denmark and northern Germany. Danish and German models show sycamore, in the most productive stands, reaching a height of 15 m in 20 years and slightly over 30 m at 80 years (Figure 5.2).

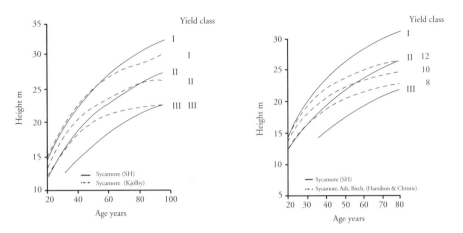

Figures 5.2 and 5.3 : Height-age graphs for sycamore from German, Danish and British growth models (SH = Schleswig - Holstein, from Nagel, 1986; Kjölby, 1958; Hamilton and Christie, 1971)

The British model (yield class 12) shows a similar top height at 20 years but only slightly more than 26 m at 80 years (see Figure 5.3).

It is noticeable, however, that the British model combines sycamore, ash and birch and this may lead to an underestimation of the growth potential of sycamore.

5.4.1.4.1 *Relative growth performance*

As potentially compatible companion species in mixtures, height growth comparisons of beech and sycamore illustrate the contrasting interspecies patterns in both the British and German models. British models for beech (yield class 10) show a top height of only 11.5 m at 20 years but a height of almost 27 m at 60 years. German models (Figure 5.4) display the slower growth for beech, with a height of only 11 m at 30 years, but the latter trend is similar to the British models.

Both German and British models demonstrate that beech begins slowly and is easily outgrown by sycamore in the early years. However, the beech overtakes sycamore at 60 years (British model) to 100 years (German model). This has silvicultural implications for planting both species in mixture if the intention is to maintain

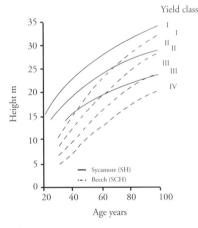

Figure 5.4: Height-age graph for sycamore and beech from German growth models, (SH = Schleswig - Holstein, from Nagel, 1986; SCH = Schober, 1971)

a sycamore stand beyond 100 years. Underplanting the sycamore with beech after the first thinning is an option to be considered in those circumstances.

The contrasting growth patterns of sycamore and beech are even more striking on viewing their mean annual (volume) increments (Figure 5.5).

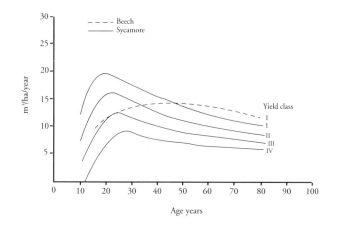

Figure 5.5: Mean annual (volume) increment curves for sycamore and beech in Denmark (from Kjölby, 1958)

According to German and Danish yield models, cumulative volume production (including thinnings) for sycamore is estimated to be around 800 - 1000 m³/ha at age 80 (Figure 5.6).

At this age British models show slightly lower volume production (766 m³/ha, Figure 5.7).

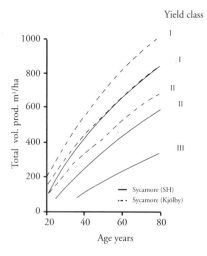

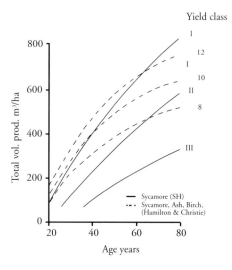

Figure 5.6: Total volume production over age for sycamore in north Germany and Denmark (SH = Schleswig - Holstein, from Nagel, 1986; Kjölby, 1958)

Figure 5.7: Total volume production for sycamore in north Germany and Britian (SH = Schleswig - Holstein, from Nagel, 1986; Hamilton and Christie, 1971)

German yield models indicate that, when grown on good sites, sycamore is much more productive than beech (Figure 5.8).

A similar pattern occurs in relation to ash (Figure 5.9) up to 100 years of age.

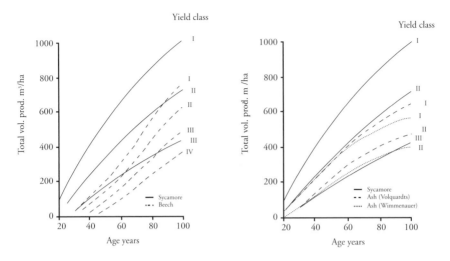

Figure 5.8: Total volume production over age for sycamore (Nagel, 1986) and beech (Schober, 1971) in north Germany

Figure 5.9: Total volume production over age for sycamore (Nagel, 1986) and ash (Volquardts, 1958; Wimmenauer, 1919)

5.4.2   Site requirements

A survey of soils at six good quality sycamore stands in Ireland clearly showed that this species can accommodate a wide range of site conditions:

(1)   a high elevation acid brown earth/brown podzolic/podzol complex at Dundalk Forest (Co. Louth);

(2)   a shallow brown podzolic over old red sandstone at Kilsheelan Forest (Co Tipperary);

(3)   a moderate gley on a relatively free-draining drumlin site at Monaghan Forest;

(4-5)   acid brown earth/brown podzolic complexes over mainly sandstone glacial till at Callan and Mullinavat Forests (Co Kilkenny); and

(6)   a grey brown podzolic developed over limestone morainic gravels and sands at Ballinasloe Forest (Co Galway).

The adaptability of sycamore to such a wide range of conditions from lowlands to uplands is favoured by its relative tolerance of frost and exposure.

A feature of the stands noted above is that they all were developed on non-calcareous topsoils, but with an increasing soil pH with depth, a maximum of pH 6.3 being recorded.

Whilst the above represents a broad sweep in terms of geography, elevation, and soil conditions, the evidence from Britain suggests that a wider range of potentially productive sycamore sites exists in this country than is perhaps appreciated. This refers in particular to calcareous soils, especially those too shallow for other broadleaf species. Sycamore grows well on a wide range of calcareous soils, including soils with calcareous unweathered material.

In Britain it is reported to grow well on neutral shale soils, on many of the heavier calcareous loams and even acid sandy soils, provided they are deep and well-drained but retain some moisture. At Bolton Estate in Yorkshire thriving plantations of sycamore are growing on thin soils over fissured limestone, similar to those of West Galway and Clare. It does best and regenerates naturally on sites where the decay of organic matter is rapid. Sycamore will not regenerate where the soil pH is less than 4, on podzols nor on heavy clays that are gleyed close to the surface. It will not tolerate stagnant water conditions; day-long flooding, particularly in summer, usually leads to deterioration in growth and wood quality.

5.4.3 Post establishment factors affecting growth and development

5.4.3.1 *Abiotic factors*

Sycamore is relatively immune to damage by late spring frost. Forking is attributed to flowering of the shoot and not to frost damage.

5.4.3.2 *Biotic factors*

Deer (fallow, red and sika) tend to browse intensively on young plants and must be controlled. Large deer populations may destroy seedlings and saplings and cause bark stripping of pole stage crops.

Sycamore is particularly prone to damage by grey squirrels. Possibly due to the relatively high sugar content of its sap, sycamore is the preferred species for bark stripping, even more so than beech. Apart from causing extensive damage to the branches this often leads to encirclement and death of the upper crown. Bark stripping damage can be severe if allowed to go unchecked (see Section 2.3.11).

Tar spot disease, caused by the fungus *Rhytisma acerinum*, frequently affects the leaves of sycamore causing premature leaf-fall. It is of little economic importance.

5.4.4 Timber properties

Sycamore is a diffuse porous wood. It is moderately hard, with a fine even texture and a natural lustre. It has medium bending and crushing strengths, low resistance to shock loads, low stiffness but has a very good steam bending classification. The wood is perishable but permeable to preservatives. Its average density at 15% moisture content is about 630 kg/m^3.

When freshly felled the wood is creamy-white in colour but weathers to a pink-brown with time. Trees should be felled and sold by the end of spring at latest to avoid deterioration and change in colour, which leads to a sharp decline in value. Rapid kiln drying helps to preserve the white colour.

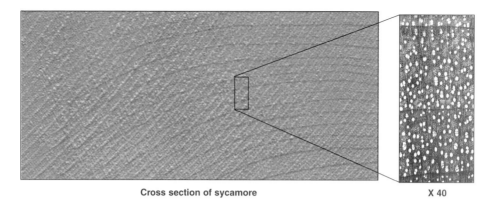

Cross section of sycamore　　　　　　　　　　　　　　**X 40**

Because of its clean white appearance and smooth finish sycamore is widely used for carving, turned bowls and tableware. It is also widely used in furniture making and flooring. Suitable logs are sliced for decorative veneers for panelling, cabinets and marquetry. Occasionally trees exhibit a wavy grain or fiddle back figure and these are usually reserved for veneer to make high-class violins and other musical instruments. They can command exceptional prices; the sale of a few such trees in Denmark during 1996 realised £1,700/m³. The development of wavy grain in sycamore is imperfectly understood, nor can its occurrence in the tree be predicted with a high level of accuracy. Experts are able to detect its presence by cutting a 'window' in the bark in order to view the wood beneath. In the log it is discernible by stripping the bark to expose the wood, which should show a 'ripple' pattern if wavy grain is present. There is nothing the silviculturist can do to promote the phenomenon. It is difficult to detect in young trees and its intensity seems to increase with age. It does not affect timber quality with regard to processing or finishing. Sycamore wood with wavy grain will usually come from large, old trees.

5.5　PRODUCTION GOALS

The objective should be the production of high quality logs suitable for veneer and sawtimber. Veneer material requires boles of 40 to 60 cm breast height diameter, which have been branch-free from an early age. On ideal sites this objective can be realised over a rotation of 60 to 80 years but may extend to 100 years on less suitable sites.

As a diffuse porous wood and in terms of its utilisation requirements, there is little or no deterioration in quality with rapid diameter growth. Therefore, it makes economic sense to select a silvicultural regime that will attain the utilisation objectives in the shortest time possible.

5.6　STAND ESTABLISHMENT

5.6.1　Site preparation

5.6.1.1　*Fencing*

Sycamore is prone to damage by rabbits and hares if left unprotected (see Section 2.3.1.1).

5.6.1.2　*Vegetation control and soil preparation (see Section 2.3.1.2)*

5.6.2   Regeneration of old woodland

Sycamore is a prolific seed bearer and produces seed every year, with mast years every two to three years. Like ash, sycamore seed is disseminated by wind and this facilitates stand regeneration even from a small number of trees (10 - 15 stems/ha). Seed ripens in September/October and is shed within a month.

Natural regeneration of sycamore can be obtained in old woodland by making use of its tendency to colonise natural openings in the canopy. The resulting naturally regenerated groups can be enlarged in the manner described for ash (see Section 4.6.2.2). However, natural regeneration will not occur on sites infested with weeds or grass. Therefore, treatment as described in Section 2.3.1.2.1 will be required.

If mature beech are present in the stand it may be preferable to wait until a beech mast year coincides with a good seed year for sycamore. This helps to ensure a sycamore/beech mixture in the regeneration, and the beech can be used to form an understorey. Alternatively, sycamore can be regenerated by the group shelterwood system in the manner described for ash (see Section 4.6.2.2).

Sycamore has the capacity to tolerate shade in the seedling stage but needs rapid release if it is to grow well. A short time period for removal of the overhead canopy (about 5 years) is recommended and this will have the effect of ensuring that shade bearers, such as beech, remain in the understorey. Sycamore/beech mixtures have silvicultural implications which will need to be addressed later in the rotation if the sycamore is to be grown beyond 80 - 100 years (see Section 5.6.3.3).

5.6.3   Afforestation

In most situations artificial regeneration of sycamore will involve the afforestation of land formerly used for agriculture. Where a plough pan has developed on former tillage ground subsoiling will be needed. Former pasture needs no site preparation other than pre-planting treatment with herbicide (see Section 2.3.1.2).

Plants normally used are 1+1 and 1+2 years old transplants. Recommendations regarding these are shown in Table 5.1.

Table 5.1: Recommended sizes for sycamore bare-rooted transplants

Organisation	Maximum age years	Minimum root collar diameter mm	Maximum root collar diameter mm	Minimum height cm	Maximum height cm
Forest Service	3	7	-	40	75
British Standards Institute	-	4.5	6	30	50

Recommendations for plant handling are given in Section 2.3.2.

5.6.3.1 *Pure sycamore stands*

Although sycamore is often a component of state broadleaved stands, pure blocks of the species are rare. However, the few known stands of mainly pure sycamore high forest are very encouraging, both in growth performance and stem quality.

Sycamore is often found growing in exposed conditions but its best growth will be attained in sheltered localities where site conditions are favourable. It grows well in pure plantations and although it will benefit from mixtures of other broadleaves, it is not a species that requires nursing. It is intolerant of competition from grasses, so weed control throughout the establishment phase is important (see Section 2.3.5).

Pure sycamore should be planted in rows 2 m apart and 1.25 m in the rows (4,000 plants/ha).

5.6.3.2 *Sycamore mixtures with conifers*

From a visual amenity aspect, larch is the favoured species in mixtures with broadleaves. It is the species that mimics broadleaves best in that it is deciduous and its light green foliage is more visually compatible with that of sycamore.

As sycamore does not require nursing, mixtures with larch are feasible only in the context of an early return from thinnings or as a permanent mixture for the whole rotation. Larch thinnings provide fencing material of good durability.

The initial rapid growth of sycamore enables it to compete with European larch in the early decades. Thereafter the larch tends to assume dominance and intervention will be necessary to maintain the mixture. Both sycamore and larch can be retained for long rotation periods without deterioration in wood quality.

Intimate mixtures can be in rows or group-wise. Groups are more visually acceptable in the landscape and, although more time consuming at planting, they offer greater flexibility of management later. Group size should be at least 100 m².

The most extensive and successful stands of sycamore in these islands are on the Bolton Estate in Yorkshire. Pioneered by the late Lord Bolton and George Stevenson, the Bolton system has been modified over the years to planting with 50% European larch and 50% sycamore, always with the intention of realising a final crop of sycamore.

In sycamore/larch mixtures the sycamore should be planted at 2 x 1.25 m and larch at 2 x 2 m.

5.6.3.3 *Sycamore mixtures with other broadleaves*

Sycamore grows well in mixture with ash, with which it has much in common in terms of site requirements, growth rate and silvicultural treatment. Beech is its natural companion species with which it will compete successfully up to about 50 years. After this age the mixture will need silvicultural intervention to favour the sycamore, otherwise it tends to be overtaken by the beech later in the rotation.

Unlike ash, sycamore can be allowed to grow on to a rotation of 120 years or more without deterioration in wood quality. A beech mixture therefore gives greater management flexibility in that it can be used both as a companion species in the upper storey or as an understorey. Crowding of the sycamore in older stands should, however, be avoided. Like ash it has poor powers of recovery once suppressed and will be eliminated from mixtures if the crowns are not kept free.

Since groups (minimum size 100 m²) give more flexibility of management in later years, mixtures should preferably be arranged group-wise, in rows 2 x 1.25 m for sycamore, and the appropriate spacing for the mixture species. A line-wise mixture is suitable, however, where beech is intended to remain as a serving species in the understorey. Lines will also provide greater protection for the frost tender beech at the establishment stage.

5.6.4   Vegetation management

Sycamore will benefit from vegetation management until the plants are at least 1m in height (see Section 2.3.5).

5.7   FORMATIVE SHAPING

Although sycamore has better apical dominance than beech and oak it is sometimes prone to forking. Such forking is stated to be associated with its floral biology and the timing and intensity of flowering; forking is induced every time a leading shoot flowers. This can have a considerable impact on tree form if corrective action is not taken by formative shaping (see Section 2.3.6).

5.8   TENDING

For crops regenerated by both natural and artificial methods, as well as sycamore/conifer mixtures, tending should take place when the crop has a top height of 7-8 m (see Section 2.3.7).

5.9   PRUNING

Sycamore's facility for natural pruning is rated as moderate. In pure stands and mixtures natural pruning should give 6 -10 m boles, free of live branches, at time of final crop tree selection (see Section 2.3.8).

5.10   THINNING

Thinning practice is dealt with in Section 2.3.9. In sycamore/larch mixtures most of the larch will be removed at the first thinning. Some well developed larch with good crowns and straight stems may be high pruned and allowed to grow to the full sycamore rotation.

Early and heavy thinning has been the practice at the Bolton Estate for sycamore/larch mixtures. The schedule aims at a reduction in stem numbers to about 150 at 30 - 35 years of age, when the crop has a top height of about 20 m. Throughout their development trees have at least 40% live crown and are virtually free growing from early youth. This ensures maximum stem diameter increment but artificial pruning has been necessary for quality wood production.

5.11   UNDERPLANTING

Sycamore, like ash, shows rapid growth for three or four decades but after 50 years height growth begins to decline. Unlike ash, the wood does not suffer from degrade at 70 - 80 years and sycamore can be grown to rotations comparable with those of beech and oak. For such long rotations the presence of an understorey will assist in controlling ground vegetation and provide silvicultural flexibility (see Section 2.3.10).

Wild Cherry

Prunus avium L.
Crann Silíní Fiáin

Wild cherry,
Black Forest

6.1 Summary

Wild cherry is one of the most valuable timber species in Europe: for centuries it has been used in the manufacture of high-class furniture. It dominated the style of furniture making during the first half of the 19th century and is still highly valued today, even in short lengths and small dimensions. Its characteristic early and spectacular flowering is highly valued by the public, who regard its blossom as 'a thing of beauty' in the landscape, especially along woodland margins. It is also considered to be a source of sustenance for many birds and insects.

It grows very rapidly in youth and develops large crowns but needs careful thinning in middle age. Because of its rapid growth and relatively short life span (70 - 80 years) it can be regarded as an ideal tree for mixtures in small woodlands, especially along the margins, where it will produce quality timber on relatively short rotations. Cherry should therefore be considered by small landowners, with suitable sites, as an additional source of income. It has the potential to be more profitable than other broadleaved species, producing three times as much revenue as beech and sycamore and over 30% more than ash. The main reasons for this are the higher timber prices as well as rapid diameter increment - if thinned properly.

6.1.1 Key characteristics

- Strong light demander, except when young
- Site specific
- Susceptible to damage by late spring frost
- Responsive to vegetation control
- Good apical dominance
- Poor ability for natural pruning
- Not susceptible to damage by grey squirrel
- Susceptible to bacterial canker and heart-rot

6.2 NATURAL DISTRIBUTION AND OCCURRENCE

Wild cherry is naturally distributed throughout Europe from the Atlantic coast to western Siberia and north to the 61st parallel. Its natural range includes Great Britain and Ireland. It reaches its optimum in subatlantic-submediterranean areas, especially in central and southern Europe but avoids regions with a continental climate.

Like other fruit producing tree species, cherry has been the source of various fruit tree cultivars for over a thousand years. Nowadays, it is almost impossible to ascertain where it was naturally distributed and where it was introduced by man. Many forest trees, even in remote areas, are influenced by garden varieties. The choice of suitable provenance has therefore become one of the crucial factors in selecting wild cherry for forestry purposes.

In Ireland, wild cherry occurs naturally as an occasional tree species, or in small groups in mixed broadleaved woodland, and in hedgerows. Its distribution is widespread throughout the island but it is generally confined to sheltered or moderately sheltered sites with fertile free-draining mineral soils. While the decorative appearance of the timber and its superior properties for wood turning have been known to foresters and craftsmen for many years, it is only recently that the species has been planted for timber production.

6.3 PROVENANCE

Little is known of the variation in the native population of cherry. An extensive survey of Coillte forests identified very few specimen trees, which would be suitable for inclusion in a breeding programme for the species. Whether this is due to poor genotypes (a species at the edge of its natural distribution), or insufficient growing space as a result of natural seeding into established forests, is not clear.

Provenance trials of cherry have not been established to date. Comparative information on the performance of Irish and continental seed sources is therefore not available. Recommending seed sources in the absence of scientific data is difficult. Experience from the Coillte broadleaf breeding programme indicates that native material may not be as vigorous as some continental sources. Selected clones from French breeding programmes have proven to be considerably more vigorous in the nursery than selected Irish material. These are available commercially as rooted cuttings and, while their performance has yet to be fully tested in Ireland, they offer a considerable improvement over the wild seedling stock from the same provenances. This would suggest that non-native material might have some potential for timber production in this country but extensive field testing is required to determine its adaptability, given the fact that frost, cankers and viruses are serious threats to the health, survival and growth of the species. If cherry is to be planted as occasional trees for timber then this material could be considered, bearing in mind the limitations mentioned above. If conservation or amenity is a priority then native Irish seed collected from the best trees should be used as a first choice.

6.4 ECOLOGICAL DEMANDS AND CHARACTERISTICS OF THE SPECIES

6.4.1 Biology, autecology and growth performance

6.4.1.1 *Biology and morphology*

Wild cherry (*Prunus avium*) is a medium sized tree species, normally 20 - 25 m in height but with the potential to reach 30 m at 100 years of age. It has strong apical dominance so it usually grows straight with monopodial form. However, because of its light demanding characteristics, crown development and stem form is often greatly influenced by competitors.

Wild cherry does not form a very compact root system. In its youth it produces a taproot but later develops a more heart-shaped system with some lateral roots. The root system, however, can be much modified by site conditions.

Wild cherry coppices quite well and is renowned for its capacity to produce sucker shoots. This is one of the reasons why it has survived so well in coppice stands on the Continent. Root suckers can be used for planting and should take preference over plant material of unknown provenance.

Wild cherry is pollinated by insects and, since it is usually self-sterile, it requires cross pollination. Pollination can be greatly hampered by cold wet weather. Consequently, even though flower production may be excellent, good seed years can be irregular. Generally good seed years occur every 1 - 3 years. The trees flower in April/May before flushing of leaves. Flower buds are formed on the short branches of the previous year. They are susceptible to damage by late spring frost.

6.4.1.2 *Seed treatment*

Fructification is abundant at 20 - 25 years but may begin as early as 5 - 8 years of age. The fruits ripen at the end of June but mostly in July, or even in August at higher altitudes. Large quantities of fruits are cleaned by using rotating macerators and water, which allows the pulp and the empty stones to be eliminated by floating and sieving. The stones can be dried to quite a low moisture content (9 - 10%) and then stored for several years.

Stratification is carried out between mid August and mid September. It is done in outdoor pits and consists of mixing equal amounts of peat, sand and seed, making sure the medium is moist. The medium is mixed thoroughly once a week until the appearance of the radicals, usually in mid February to early March. If sowing is not possible at this stage the medium (including seeds) may be stored at a temperature of - 3°C for up to 10 weeks. It is important to ensure that defrosting takes place slowly before sowing.

The weight of 1,000 stones (seeds) ranges from 125 - 166 g.

In natural conditions the seed is disseminated by birds.

As a tree species of the subatlantic-submediterranean climatic regions wild cherry shows a marked preference for warm and sunny sites. It is susceptible to damage by late spring frosts and may suffer from deep winter frosts. It has average water requirements and is relatively tolerant of drought stress. Fluctuating soil moisture content is acceptable but not a high water-table nor flooding lasting more than a few days. The soil should have a medium to high nutrient status and should preferably be derived from calcareous parent material.

Like ash, wild cherry is relatively shade tolerant in its early years. However, even then it needs sufficient light to grow satisfactorily. From the thicket stage onwards it becomes a strong light demander and requires adequate growing space.

6.4.1.4   *Growth performance*

Wild cherry, like ash, shows very rapid growth in the early years. When planted on suitable sites it can attain 20 - 80 cm height increment in its second growing season. Annual height growth culminates between 7 and 15 years of age and slows down appreciably between 30 and 40 years. From then on its capacity to respond to increased growing space is markedly reduced.

Studies in Northrhine-Westphalia (north-west Germany) show maximum mean annual volume increment for pure wild cherry stands in the range 4.5 - 7.5 m³/ha/year. British yield models show slightly greater values of 4.9 - 9.1 m³/ha/year. Although these yields may be disappointing, the high end-value for the produce more than compensates for this relatively low volume production.

Preliminary yield data for pure wild cherry stands on good sites are shown in Table 6.1.

Table 6.1: Preliminary yield models for wild cherry on good sites in Germany and Britain, (Anon 1993; Pryor, 1988)

COUNTRY	Age years	Top height m	Mean diameter cm	Stocking trees/ha	Main crop volume m³/ha	Mean annual increment m³/ha/year
GERMANY	20	13.7	12	960	47	3.3
	30	19.0	20	502	106	5.7
	40	23.0	28	300	163	6.9
	50	26.0	37	196	207	7.5
	60	28.4	45	135	235	7.5
BRITAIN	20	12.5	12	1,950	117	5.9
	30	17.5	17	1,030	178	7.4
	40	21.0	22	670	241	8.4
	50	23.1	28	445	283	8.9
	60	24.1	34	310	310	9.1
	70	24.5	41	220	327	9.1
	80	24.7	49	165	349	9.0

Data from Germany are derived from dense stands that have not been properly thinned. The British tables are based on a study in which measurement data were collected from more than 40 stands throughout Britain. Stocking densities for a given top height are even higher than in the German table, so it is likely that they too have not been adequately thinned. It is suggested that modern thinning regimes would result in more rapid diameter growth.

Both sets of data reflect the very rapid height growth of wild cherry during the first 40 years, followed by a sharp decrease in subsequent years. Studies in Britain indicate that, over this 40-year period, rates of height growth are comparable with those of conifers of yield class 14 - 18. In Freiburg (Germany) wild cherry competes successfully with Douglas fir for the first 30 years.

Simulated height growth curves, relative to a range of broadleaves and conifers, are shown for southern Germany in Figure 6.1.

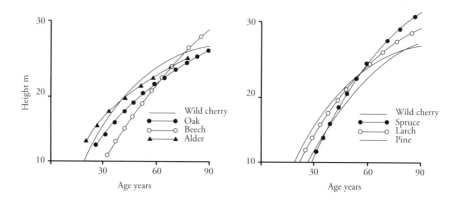

Figure 6.1: Comparative height growth of (a) cherry and other broadleaves and (b) cherry and a range of conifers (Spiecker, 1994)

6.4.2   Site requirements

The wild cherry is primarily a tree of brown earths and loamy calcareous soils. It grows best on deep slightly moist soils, preferably with some lime content, of a medium to high nutrient status.

However, according to recent studies in Germany the practice of restricting it to the best limestone sites is no longer tenable. Nutrients do not appear to be a limiting factor as long as they and the moisture supply are not too low.

Its occasional occurrence on relatively dry and shallow soils is primarily due to reduced competition from other broadleaves. On such sites productivity is invariably low. Therefore, shallow rocky soils, even when calcareous, cannot be recommended for wild cherry plantations.

Because of its relatively poor rooting ability, compacted soils will also lead to poor growth. Acid soils, and soils with a high water-table or subject to periodic flooding, are unsuitable and should be avoided.

6.4.3 Post establishment factors affecting growth and development

6.4.3.1 *Abiotic factors*

Wild cherry does not grow well on exposed sites. Because of its superficial rooting habit it is prone to wind damage when it reaches heights of 4 - 5 m above slower growing species. Moreover, trees with compressed crowns in underthinned stands may easily become victims of gales. Careful selection of sites, excluding all wet soil types, and timely thinning, will alleviate the problem.

Snow damage is almost unknown.

Cherry is one of the earliest broadleaves to flower, and as a consequence is susceptible to late spring frosts, particularly at the establishment phase. The leaves emerge later and are damaged much less frequently. Damage by early frost is rare as the trees complete their shoot growth between the end of June and mid July. The shoots are therefore hardened-off sufficiently by autumn.

Bacterial camker in wild cherry, caused by *Pseudomonas syringae*

6.4.3.2 *Biotic factors*

On the Continent wild cherry is vulnerable to attack by mice during the year of planting and in the following years. Damage is most severe in dense grass swards, which offer excellent cover for mice. Vegetation control and management (see Sections 6.6.2.1 and 6.6.3), therefore, also offers a very effective means of mice control.

In contrast to other broadleaves there is no recorded incidence of attack by grey squirrel on wild cherry. It is, however, vulnerable to fraying and browsing by deer, although natural regeneration usually escapes serious damage.

The only insect pest recorded on wild cherry in Britain is the cherry blackfly (*Myzus cerasi*). Leaf curl and shoot distortion is attributed to this insect, and severe infestations can result in death of the terminal bud and forking in the early years after planting.

The wild cherry is prone to a number of diseases. Bacterial canker, (caused by *Pseudomonas syringae*) is usually more serious in planted cherry. It is characterised by exudation of gum from areas of bark. The cankerous lesions that develop may encircle the stem, resulting in the death of the tree. Pruning wounds facilitate infection so pruning should be done in the period June to August when infection of woody material is least likely. If the bacteria are present in a stand, removal of infected branches, or even the infected tree, may effect some control.

Some viruses can cause similar symptoms in wild cherry but ornamental and fruiting cherries are more likely to be affected.

Silver leaf is a major fungal disease of fruit orchards but is unlikely to become a problem in forest species.

Stem rot of wild cherry may lead to financial loss. The rot-causing fungi may enter the stem through the heartwood of dead or pruned branches, causing decay of the stem below the point of entry. Alternatively, the fungi may enter through the roots and, in contrast to branch/stem rot, progress slowly upwards. Normally it does not reach the higher parts of the stem. This rot usually attacks the inner core of the stem causing heart-rot. Because the centre core is invariably knotty a small amount of heart-rot is not too serious a degrade. Heart-rot is usually confined to older trees and this points to the need to harvest them before they deteriorate.

In Britain, heart-rot in wild cherry is stated to be economically devastating and is much more serious than any of the other diseases. It is often a race against time to bring the trees to sawlog size before the onset of heart-rot.

Among the fungi causing rot are the honey fungus (*Armillaria mellea*) and 'Fomes' (*Heterobasidion annosum*), making control extremely difficult. The best approach is to avoid planting wild cherry on unsuitable sites. Reports suggest that severe heart-rot is more likely in trees growing on compacted and shallow soils. Presumably soils that are shallow or subject to waterlogging, often cause dieback of crown and roots. Windthrow is often more prevalent on such sites, probably as a consequence of root decay.

6.4.4 Timber properties

Wild cherry is classified as a semi-ring porous wood. The earlywood contains fine vascular tissues close together while those of the latewood are less dense. Therefore, annual rings can be easily distinguished.

The change from heartwood to sapwood is less distinguishable. The narrow sapwood has a yellowish-reddish colour. When fresh the heartwood is only slightly darker but this intensifies under the influence of light to give a light golden-reddish brown tone. It is then highly decorative.

Sawn timber must be seasoned carefully, preferably weighted, as it has a tendency to warp. However, once dried it is fairly stable. The timber is moderately hard with a fine texture. It is readily machinable and works easily to give a very good finish. It has very good wood-bending properties and takes stains and most finishes well. Fresh weight is 900 kg/m³ and air-dry weight (12 - 15% moisture content) is 600 kg/m³.

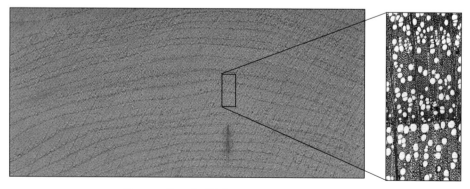

Cross section of wild cherry   **X 40**

Log sizes down to 24 cm top diameter are acceptable by the furniture trade in Britain. Planking logs require a mid-diameter greater than 35 cm and veneer logs are usually over 45 cm. Price increases with diameter and quality. Veneer logs must be at least 2.7 m long, free of all defects and have a desirable colour. Defects cause the log to be downgraded from veneer to sawlog quality, with a related decrease in price. Prime planking and veneer logs must be entirely free of knots and other blemishes. In Britain, narrow rings (1.5 - 4 mm) are usually more acceptable for veneer but wood with much wider rings is acceptable for planking. Knots, tension wood (in leaning trees), spiral grain and gum pockets (from occluded wounds) are frequent causes of degrade.

The use of wild cherry in the construction of massive furniture is today impractical in terms of material requirement and cost. When quality is suitable its use for veneer is more the norm.

6.5 PRODUCTION GOALS

In addition to increasing the diversity of tree species in the landscape, wild cherry provides high value timber. It has been steadily favoured by timber buyers for several decades in Britain and on the Continent. With hardwood logs from the tropics becoming more difficult to obtain, it is safe to assume that the demand for quality home-grown hardwoods, such as wild cherry, will continue to increase.

In Germany the stems are normally harvested over a wide region and transported to a central depot. There they are presented to the potential purchasers and sold by auction. High priced stems (in excess of £400/m³) showed the following characteristics:

- lengths greater than 6 m;

- mean mid diameter greater than 40 cm underbark;

- knots present only in the stem centre core of less than 10 cm;

- logs free of rot or with stem rot of the centre core not exceeding 10 cm.

Annual ring widths tend to vary over a wide range and may even reach 8 - 10 mm. This, however, does not imply a reduction in value for such timber; such ring widths are quite acceptable. In sharp contrast to oak, it is possible to produce high value wild cherry timber over a period of 50 - 80 years. This shows the attractiveness of cherry management in private forestry.

6.6 SILVICULTURE AND MANAGEMENT

6.6.1 Natural regeneration

Naturally regenerated wild cherry is distributed solely by birds. Where wild cherry occurs naturally in a stand of other species it should be retained as an important mixture component. If necessary, it should be released in tending and early thinning, by removing competitors of other tree species. Protection of single plants by individual tree guards may be desirable (see Section 6.6.2.2).

6.6.2 Artificial regeneration

There are very few areas where the forest manager can rely on natural regeneration of this rare species. Therefore, artificial regeneration is the norm.

6.6.2.1 *Site preparation*

Ground preparation by strip ploughing or vegetation control with herbicide to reduce weed competition can be advantageous against the rodent population and may help to ease planting (see Section 2.3.1.2).

6.6.2.2 *Fencing*

Frequently, wild cherry will be planted in small groups in a matrix of other species, which will require fencing. More extensive pure plantations of wild cherry may either be fenced or left unfenced, in accordance with local conditions but generally it will be necessary to provide stock fencing, at least. Normally, the young plants will escape damage because of the taller plant material used (greater than 1 m) and the rapid height growth in the second year after planting. Where rabbit and hare populations are large, the use of spiral tree guards to protect individual stems may prove more economical than fencing the area.

Deer find the foliage highly palatable and cause severe damage by fraying saplings. Depending on the extent of the wild cherry (small groups or plantation) control by culling, individual tree protection or deer fencing will be necessary.

6.6.3 Vegetation control and soil preparation

Spot application of glyphosate or the treatment of a 1 m strip gives excellent vegetation control (see Section 2.3.1.2). This may significantly reduce frost damage, an important consideration for this frost tender species.

6.6.4 Afforestation

6.6.4.1 *Planting stock*

Normally, 2+0 year seedlings or alternatively 1+1 or 2+1 year old transplants, of a height of 50 - 120 cm are used. Smaller sizes should be discarded. Plants with desiccated or damaged leaders should be rejected since they will usually result in stems with deep forks. Large, recently lifted plants, and good planting technique and attention in the early years, will reduce or even eliminate subsequent filling-in.

6.6.4.2 *Spacing and establishment of mixtures*

Recently established spacing experiments with wild cherry include a range of densities from as high as 10,000 to as low as 400 plants/ha but guidelines for optimum densities have yet to be formulated. Recommendations for current practice are between 2,000 and 4,000 plants/ha (2.25 x 2 m - 2 x 1.25 m) depending on the size and quality of the planting stock.

Wild cherry can be mixed with other broadleaved species such as beech, or hornbeam, which may act as an understorey. Because of its rapid early growth but relatively short rotation period it is able to provide some early revenue. Therefore, it is valuable as a group mixture in stands of oak, ash or sycamore. It should be borne in mind, however, that the growth habits of sycamore and ash show many similarities with cherry and may sometimes become competitors even at an early stage.

Wild cherry is recommended as a suitable mixture tree in small gaps where natural regeneration of beech (especially) does not sufficiently cover the whole area. Within these gaps a planting espacement of 2 x 2 m is recommended. Since beech reaches its culmination of height growth only at 30 - 50 years of age, problems of competition for cherry do not occur before mid-rotation age. The less competitive the cherry, relative to the beech on a particular site, the larger the groups of cherry should be.

Mixtures with oaks are less problematic, especially when mixed in rows or narrow bands; they can be regarded as temporary mixtures.

Single trees or small groups of a few wild cherry are recommended at woodland edges. Here the trees can be harvested when of sufficiently large diameters, without causing damage to the remaining stems.

6.6.4.3   *Tending and thinning*

As stated above, wild cherry grows very fast in the first two decades and is normally well ahead of all other competitors during this period. However, on losing this dominance, it becomes highly sensitive to any crown competition and reacts immediately by a reduction in both diameter and volume increment. Therefore, the aim should be to retain a live crown depth of half or even two thirds of the tree height.

Where plantations have been established with relatively small numbers of plants, singling of forked leaders and removal of large branches is recommended even as early as the second year after planting. This should concentrate on the best specimens only (not more than 200 trees/ha) and should be continued by artificial pruning (see Section 6.6.4.4.) to maintain a branch-free stem length of half the tree height.

At a top height of 6 - 8 m (age 7 - 9 years) tending measures begin by cutting out all trees competing with some 200 potential final crop candidates/ha (about 7 m apart). Where appropriate, cherry should be released by selective removal of competitors to ensure that the crowns have adequate growing space and are not in contact with each other.

Up to a top height of 15 m (age about 22 years) thinning should take place on a three-year cycle. This is later extended to a five-year cycle. However, this should not be interpreted too rigidly. The development of the individual tree crowns should be the main guide (see Section 2.3.9).

6.6.4.4   *Pruning*

Recent investigations show that wild cherry can tolerate green pruning. Indeed, green pruning is more or less essential as the basis for the production of high quality timber in relatively short periods. Even at relatively close spacing cherry does not have the ability to prune itself naturally. Although branches will die when shaded by competitors, they are retained on the stem for many years after their deaths. This leads to the formation of dead knots in the wood and eventually results in a serious degrade of the timber.

Pruning should be done when the branch diameter is less than 3 cm at the junction of branch and stem. For wild cherry, this usually means pruning live branches long before they are killed by shading. If branches are allowed to attain larger diameters than 3 cm, they are in danger of forming heartwood and their death or removal then will provide direct access for decay fungi into the heartwood of the tree. Since there is a direct relationship between spacing and branch diameter, wider spacing will necessitate more frequent pruning. As a general rule green pruning of wild cherry will be necessary every three to four years on good sites, up to a minimum height of 6 m.

Pruning in stages up to at least 6 m stem height is necessary while, at the same time, keeping the crown length to at least 50% of tree height. Pruning should be carried out from June to August, when the tree is in full sap. When possible, a long-handled secateurs should be used, so that the pruning wounds will be smaller and less rough than those resulting from the use of a pruning-saw. The branch is cut, perpendicular to its axis, close to the stem so that the smallest possible pruning wounds arise. Only the 80 - 130 final crop trees/ha should be pruned up to 6 m. High pruning up to 10 m is possible on a maximum of 80 final crop trees/ha on good sites. It may then be necessary to prolong the rotation period slightly.

At a top height of 23 m (about 40 years of age), the stand should consist of 80 - 130 crop trees/ha, with the potential to reach diameters of 52 - 60 cm at breast height over a rotation period of 70 - 80 years. These will have been pruned to at least 6 m.

Beech

Fagus sylvatica L.
Feá

Beech, Terenure, Dublin

7.1. Summary

Beech produces a highly versatile hardwood. It has excellent woodworking properties and forms the mainstay of the furniture industry. Good quality logs are used in high-class joinery and veneer. On the Continent it is regarded as the timber most likely to substitute for the decreasing supply of tropical woods.

Beech has the capacity to grow well under a wide range of site conditions, from acid to alkaline, provided the nutrient status is satisfactory. It will not tolerate waterlogging and is subject to windthrow on gleyed soils. It prefers a moist climate with annual rainfall exceeding 750 mm.

Beech is difficult to establish on open exposed sites without overhead shelter and is prone to damage by late (spring) frost. This results in forking of the leader. Once established, however, it is relatively easy to manage. It is the most shade tolerant of the broadleaves and forms an excellent understorey to other species. It also has the potential to create pure stands of high quality. In mixture with other species it will begin slowly but later in the rotation it will outgrow and dominate most species if corrective action is not taken. Beech has an economic rotation of 100 - 120 years.

7.1.1 Key Characteristics

- Good shade tolerance
- Susceptible to damage by late spring frost
- Preference for base rich sites
- Prone to coarse growth and forking
- Medium ability for natural pruning
- Susceptible to grey squirrel damage

7.1.2 General silvicultural treatment

Top height m	Stocking after treatment trees/ha	Comment
0.2 - 1.0	6,600	Planted at 2.0 x 0.75 m / (2 m between rows).
2 - 3	6,000	Formative shaping - singling of forked leaders.
4 - 5	5,500	2nd formative shaping (if necessary).
5 - 8	2,500 - 3,000	Tending - remove wolves to encourage development of 1,000 potential crop trees/ha.
12 - 15	1,500	Heavy crown thinning. Select 150 final crop trees/ha.
15 - 30		Thin to remove competitors (2 - 3 stems/final crop tree) at intervals of 2 - 3 m height growth.
30 - 35	100 - 120	Fell final crop at 40 - 60 cm breast height diameter.

7.2 NATURAL DISTRIBUTION AND OCCURRENCE

Of the thirty species of beech, which inhabited the northern hemisphere during the Tertiary Period, only ten now remain. Among them is the one beech species of the European Continent, *Fagus sylvatica.* Beech was by far the most dominant tree species of western and central Europe in early times, before being subjected to severe pressure by human activity. Without interference by man, it would again assume that dominance.

The European beech is well adapted to a maritime climate. It is indigenous to most of the temperate parts of Europe, from Norway to the Mediterranean and from northern Spain to the Caucasus (Figure 7.1).

Good quality plantation beech (100 years old), Laubach, Hessen, Germany

Figure 7.1: Natural distribution of beech

Continental climate determines its eastern boundary. In Mediterranean regions it occurs only at higher elevations, where the climate is sufficiently oceanic, as for instance on the slopes of Mount Etna in Sicily at 1,200 - 2,000 m. In western and central Europe it inhabits a wide range of sites, from sandy to very rich soils, provided soil moisture or air humidity satisfies its requirements. However, it avoids permanent or periodically wet sites such as swamps, moors and riverine soils on the one hand and extremely dry sites, like very poor sands and shallow rendzinas, on the other.

It is native to the south of England and is now naturalised throughout Britain and Ireland.

Beech was introduced to Ireland probably in the late 16th century and formed a substantial component of estate plantations for aesthetics and commercial use during the 17th century. Many of the older trees date from that period and are now over 200 years old.

State planting of beech began in the early 1930s and most of the beech plantations were established between then and 1955. Beech now constitutes one-third of Coillte broadleaved forest, amounting to over 5,600 ha. The conventional approach was to plant the beech in mixture with European larch or Scots pine, at a stocking density of 4,400 - 5,200 plants/ha, either in 50/50 line mixtures or occasionally 75% conifer and 25% beech (one line in four).

Over time the conifers were removed and these plantations are now essentially pure beech stands.

Examples of these original beech/conifer mixtures can be found on low hills across the midlands, on the thin soils overlying fissured limestone in Galway and Clare and in the east, in Wicklow and Wexford. With few exceptions the sites share a common feature in that they are free draining. This applies even to those sites on drumlins in Monaghan and Cavan.

PROVENANCE

As mentioned above, beech has formed a large component of estate planting and today is one of the major broadleaved tree species in our landscape. Since many estate owners had properties in both Ireland and England, the original seed sources of beech almost certainly were imported from England. As with the other major broadleaved species our knowledge of local provenance variation in beech is limited. Also, the performance of home sources relative to continental origins is unknown. The fact that beech is not native to Ireland may mean that we do not have the best sources in our home grown stands.

Since its introduction, importation of beech seed is likely to have occurred on a regular basis, at least until the first plantings matured in the middle to late 19th century. Records show that importations continued from the start of the state forestry programme over the 50-year period prior to 1980. During this time 34% of all beech seed sown was imported, mostly from Germany and Austria, in the years prior to World War II. During the 1960s imports were mainly from Romania, Bulgaria and Czechoslovakia. Home collections amounted to 31,000 kg, or 68% of total sowings, over this 50-year period. Most of this material was collected in the 1940s and 1950s. Collections took place in many forests without rigorous selection of stands or seed trees. To what extent this practice has resulted in the poor stem form seen in many beech plantations is difficult to determine but it is almost certain to have had some effect.

Provenance trials have been established comparing the performance of home collected seed to imported origins. These should in time provide the answer. Stem form is a highly heritable trait and while genetics play an important part in determining the quality of a stand, silvicultural practice (use of mixtures, thinning) can modify or improve the form of stands of lesser genetic quality. However, starting with good seed sources will result in lower inputs being required and ultimately in a higher quality crop. As with all species attention paid to selecting the correct provenance and the quality of seed trees will be repaid handsomely in the future.

Beech is a large-seeded broadleaved species and mast can only be stored for a relatively short period of time without significant loss in viability (storage for longer periods requires special treatment - see Section 7.4.1.2). Mast years in Ireland occur infrequently and intervals of between 5 -15 years are not uncommon. While it is desirable and recommended to use seed from registered seed stands in Ireland, imports are necessary to provide a continuous supply for the planting programme. In the absence of firm comparative data from our provenance trials, sources from registered seed stands in the northern regions of Germany and France, UK, Belgium, Denmark and the Netherlands are suitable alternatives to home sources. As the trials mature more precise recommendations can be given.

Most of the mature beech stands in Ireland have been high-graded (the best stems removed) over the years and while good genotypes would have been removed their genes still exist in the remaining population although at a lower frequency.

Beech regenerates freely and naturally in Ireland and an opportunity exists to restore lost genotypes by natural regeneration. The high numbers of plants/ha in naturally regenerated stands provide the opportunity for intensive selection of trees with good form which are well adapted and productive in Irish conditions. Where appropriate, natural regeneration should be the preferred method of regenerating broadleaved stands, since it offers many benefits in terms of genetics, silviculture and the environment.

7.4 ECOLOGICAL DEMANDS AND CHARACTERISTICS OF THE SPECIES

7.4.1 Biology, autecology and growth performance

7.4.1.1 *Biology and tree form*

Beech is one of the most outstanding broadleaved trees of Europe. It prefers a maritime climate with high humidity and precipitation exceeding 750 mm/annum. When this is accompanied by soils of high nutrient status, beech can attain good to very good production and on optimal sites reach a maximum height of 40 m. Its physical life span, however, is relatively short in comparison with oak, rarely exceeding 350 years.

The crown of the beech is of such remarkable plasticity that, in exceptional circumstances, it can reach crown diameters in excess of 20 m. Crown development varies according to the growing space available; in youth, this can be greatly influenced by an overstorey. Beech may adopt a monopodial growth habit, with associated fastigiate branching, when competing with neighbours in even-aged and relatively dense stands. The greater the available growing space, the more the branches tend towards the horizontal. Young beech will extend their branches into every gap in their vicinity, giving rise to irregularly shaped crowns. Unfortunately, from a silvicultural point of view, beech stems are often deformed, and sympodial twisting is a common occurrence.

Young beech trees show better stem form when developing under the light shade of the overstorey of mature trees. There they may grow up perfectly straight, although on occasions stem twisting will still develop. Branches are shed more freely if the trees grow up in dense stands.

Trees under stress from competitors tend to develop epicormic branching. This applies in particular to intermediate and suppressed individuals. Those released later by thinning can develop large crowns but existing epicormic branches grow to form large branches. This downgrades the value of the stem.

During the first three years young beech forms a sturdy taproot, but then starts to develop an intensively twisted heart-shaped root system. This root system varies according to soil properties and may, on gleys, resolve into a very shallow aggregation in the upper 10 cm. On fissured limestone sites a highly plastic root system can develop which penetrates deep into the fissures in search of moisture and nutrients.

Under favourable growth conditions beech is windfirm. However, it may be damaged by summer gales when in full leaf or destabilised on soils waterlogged after prolonged heavy rainfall.

The oval shaped leaves are arranged alternately. Buds flush mid April to mid May. Unlike oak a second flush in June is rare and consequently, beech has a somewhat limited capacity to replace young leaves damaged by late spring frost or insects.

Beech is a monoecious species with separate male and female flowers on the same tree. The female flowers are surrounded by a four-lobed involucre and usually occur in pairs on a short stalk. Its sepals form a cupule, which opens on ripening to release two triangular shaped nuts.

Flowering is induced by very warm and dry weather in July/August, when the new buds are formed. Mast years, therefore, rely on climatic conditions during the previous year's late summer. The more maritime the climate, the less likely the occurrence of such conditions.

Fructification depends on the position of the tree in the canopy. The earliest age for open grown trees to bear seed is 40 - 50 years; in closed stands this is extended to 50 - 80 years.

7.4.1.2   *Seed collection and storage*

Seeds ripen in September to October and fall up to November. The most common method of harvesting is collection by hand from the ground but nylon nets and pierced plastic sheets can also be used. The first nuts to fall should be avoided, as they are usually empty or damaged by parasites. Moisture content of seed when collected is usually between 25 - 32%. For over-winter storage the nuts are slightly dried and stored at 3°C until spring. Storage at this temperature combined with high moisture content is sufficient to overcome dormancy and the seed can be sown in spring without any pre-treatment. If storage for a longer period is planned (up to 6 years), then it is essential that the moisture content is reduced to 8 - 9% before the seed is stored in sealed containers at - 5 to - 10°C.

Beech nuts in long term storage need to be re-moistened to 30 - 34% moisture content at 3°C for a period prior to sowing. The upper moisture limit is critical and should not be exceeded. Beech nuts are relatively heavy, weighing about 150 to 300 g/1000 nuts.

Although the ability of beech to regenerate from stool shoots is much less than other broadleaves, such as oak and ash, it has been coppiced on a greater scale in mountainous regions of continental Europe. Young beech, which have been badly damaged during extraction operations, are frequently cut back to ground level to take advantage of this capacity for sprouting. It results in the formation of shoots of much better shape (see Section 7.6.2.1).

7.4.1.3   *Autecology*

As already outlined, beech is a typical maritime species, well adapted to the climate of western and central Europe and to higher elevations in the east. It tolerates high temperatures only when not combined with long dry periods.

Young beech is very susceptible to damage by late spring frost, and may be killed because of its limited capacity to generate a second flush of leaves. Even if the trees survive, growth may be retarded for years. In locations where the occurrence of late frost is frequent, such as hollows or flat terrain, young beech should be raised only under the shelter of old stands or introduced nurse trees. Without shelter, reforestation of clearcut areas or afforestation with beech can lead to total failure on such sites. Moreover, late frost can inhibit fructification by destroying the young flowers even on large trees. Heavy winter frost can harm beech but this applies only at the borders of its distribution in eastern Europe. It is less inclined to lammas growth than oak but this feature, when it occurs, makes it more prone to damage by early autumn frost, with consequent forking. This applies especially in maritime climates, where the shoots and buds have not had sufficient time to undergo a hardening-off process before the onset of frost.

Beech is a climax species and is the most shade tolerant of all European broadleaves. Even among conifers, only silver fir and yew are more shade tolerant; these are therefore the only species able to compete with beech. Under natural conditions on the European Continent all other species find their niches on sites that are either not favourable for beech or in gaps created by wind, where they can establish themselves more quickly than beech. In Ireland, there is evidence that all suitable sites would also have been dominated by beech, had it reached this country before the land bridges disappeared. Even now, it has begun its advance in different parts of the country, in the shelter of existing stands.

7.4.1.4　*Growth performance*

Beech shows the typical growth pattern of a climax species. Height growth begins relatively slowly but continues more steadily and for much longer than pioneers such as ash (Figure 7.2).

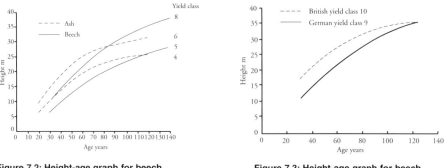

Figure 7.2: Height-age graph for beech (Schober, 1967) and ash (Volquardts,1958) in Germany

Figure 7.3: Height-age graph for beech from British (Hamilton and Christie, 1971) and German (Schober, 1967) models

Growth performance is greatly influenced by site quality.

British yield models show a maximum yield class of 10, while German models indicate a total volume production, which converts to 9 m³/ha/year at most. The British models display a more rapid growth in youth and middle age, and both tend to converge at 120 years (Figure 7.3). Current height growth culminates around 35 years in the German model and somewhat earlier in the British model. Current annual and mean annual volume increments culminate at 60 years and after 140 years respectively for the German model and at 45 years and 75 years respectively for the British model.

Beech is often outgrown by other species in the early decades but is usually able to survive under their canopies. During the second half of the rotation the roles are reversed and the resurgent beech begins to restrict the crown development of the companion species. Compared with all other broadleaved species in Europe it has the unique ability to adopt, even at a great age, a more horizontal branching habit, and thereby to enlarge the volume of its crown. It responds much better to crown thinning at an advanced age, and is therefore regarded as the most flexible tree species of our forests.

Little is known about the growth habits of provenances but there are differences in ecotypes with regard to time of flushing and leaf fall. Provenances from higher elevations flush earlier when brought to the lowlands and are therefore more susceptible to frost damage.

7.4.2   Site requirements

Unlike ash, beech has the capacity to grow well under a wide range of soil conditions, from acid to alkaline. It will grow well on acid topsoils, provided there is no waterlogging in the growing season and the base (and pH) levels increase with soil depth. In such situations (acid topsoil) beech is much less demanding than ash. The soil studies (Table 7.1) showed good growth of beech on acid topsoils where there was a rapid rise in pH towards neutrality (pH 7.0) with increasing depth and higher (but not exceeding about pH 8.2).

Table 7.1: Acid topsoils showing good growth of beech

Portlaoise Forest (Co Laois)		Virginia Forest (Co Westmeath[1])		Cong Forest (Co Mayo)	
Soil depth cm	pH	Soil depth cm	pH	Soil depth cm	pH
0-5/7	4.7	0-20/25	4.4	0-20/25	5.5
5/7-20	5.4	20/25-50	5.5	20/25-50	5.7
20-35/40	6.0	50-80	8.0	75-80	7.5
35/40-50	8.0	80+	8.1		
50+	8.2				

Beech shows its best growth on soils with calcareous topsoils, preferably having a pH status from slightly acid (pH 6.0) to moderately alkaline (pH 7.5). Such soils tend to be grey brown podzolics or brown earths of high base status.

In the study such soils were found at Rathdangan Forest (Co Kildare), Broadford Forest (Co Clare) and Callan Forest (Co Kilkenny). Details are shown in Table 7.2.

Table 7.2: Calcareous topsoils showing good growth of beech

Rathdangan Forest (Co Kildare)		Broadford Forest (Co Clare)		Callan Forest (Co Kilkenny)	
Soil depth cm	pH	Soil depth cm	pH	Soil depth cm	pH
0-15	7.2	0-5/7	6.5	0-13	6.2
15-35	7.6	5/7-15	6.8	13-37	7.4
35+	7.8	15-20/30	6.8	37-62	7.5
		20/30+	8.0	62-90	7.6

Beech will not grow well, however, if the topsoil is excessively calcareous, when extremely high levels of free calcium carbonate are present. Such levels are more prone to exist if unweathered material from the subsoil or parent material is near the soil surface, which will usually have a pH of 7.5 or more. Establishment and early growth of beech may be good or reasonable on these very shallow calcareous soils. However, when the stands reach the canopy closure stage they are predisposed to growth problems, due to an inability of the roots to absorb sufficient iron and manganese.

[1] Mullaghmeen property, Co Westmeath

Satisfactory growth of beech can however be obtained on low-pH soils, and examples are found at Virginia Forest (Co Cavan), Bunclody Forest (Co Wexford), and Fermoy Forest (Co Cork) (Table 7.3).

Table 7.3: Acid topsoils where beech has grown satisfactorily

Virginia Forest (Co Cavan[1])		Bunclody Forest (Co Kilkenny)		Fermoy Forest (Co Cork)	
Soil depth		Soil depth		Soil depth	
cm	pH	cm	pH	cm	pH
0-20	4.5	0-10	4.6	0-15	4.3
20-40	4.5	10-50	4.4	15-23	4.4
40-80	4.5	50-75	4.7	23-40	4.6
80+	4.8	75+	4.9	40-65	4.8

A feature of all the sites, where beech is growing successfully, is the very sheltered conditions prevailing, leading to the conclusion that for beech, and probably for other species also, the availability of favourable shelter conditions can compensate to a considerable extent for shortcomings in soil requirements. A further point is that, despite the satisfactory growth of beech on low-pH soils, oak may well prove to be a more suitable species selection on these sites.

Whilst beech normally does best where the soil is deep, experience in Ireland is that quality beech can be produced on relatively shallow soils.

For example, excellent beech was found at Rathdangan Forest (Co Kildare), at Broadford Forest (Co Clare), and at Callan Forest (Co Kilkenny), even though the depth to the parent material did not exceed 40 cm (topsoil plus subsoil depth did not exceed 40 cm) in any of the soil profiles investigated at those sites. It appears that these soils have enough fine material (clay and silt) in the overall soil to maintain sufficient levels of soil moisture to sustain growth in periods of low rainfall. Thus, a useful rule-of-thumb is as follows: for successful growth of beech, soils should be deep where the soil is coarse-textured and has a lower capacity to retain moisture. The converse also applies: soils can be shallower if soils are moisture-retentive.

Economic considerations would indicate that beech should be restricted to moist free-draining soils of pH 6.0 - 7.5, with a good to moderate base status. It will tolerate lower pH if the moisture regime and nutrient status are adequate. Soils at the extremities of the range (heavy clay soils and poor sandy soils) should be avoided, except in locations where beech is used as a serving species in mixtures, to encourage natural pruning of the principal species (such as oak) or provide protection against the invasion of weeds. On brown earth/surface water gley intergrade soils beech, as a principal species, is prone to windthrow as it approaches maturity.

7.4.3 Post establishment factors affecting growth and development

7.4.3.1 *Abiotic factors*

As mentioned above beech has a plastic root system. On soils of high fertility it roots mainly in the upper horizons but on fissured limestone its roots grow deep into the fissures. On the latter soils it can therefore show a high degree of wind stability.

Beech, in common with ash, is very sensitive to late spring frost but unlike ash it lacks the early vigour to get its leader above the frost level. Furthermore, it flushes earlier and the risk of frost damage is therefore more acute. Delayed hardening-off in autumn can also result in frost damage to the leading bud and lead to forking. Planting on open ground subject to frost, without overhead shelter, is not recommended.

[1] Headfort property, Co Cavan

7.4.3.2   *Biotic factors*

Beech ranks next to sycamore in terms of preference by grey squirrels. Stands may be attacked from the thicket stage up to 60 years of age by gnawing away the bark from the stem, usually near the base of trees but often from larger branches in the crown. All such damage introduces a defect in the wood and may lead to fungal invasion (see Section 2.3.11).

Browsing, fraying and bark stripping by red and fallow deer can lead to serious damage where deer populations are large. In European forests damage by deer is the major problem.

Many decay fungi attack beech, among them *Polyporus* and *Ganoderma* spp. which lead to branch and butt rot, particularly of old over-mature trees. Young trees may be infested by the beech woolly aphid, which can lead to serious damage on some sites.

The one serious disease of beech reported from Britain and the Continent tends to occur on trees that have previously been subjected to stress due to long drought periods or other causes. The weakened condition of these trees makes them more vulnerable to attack by insects (including aphids) and fungi. The disease (beech bark disease) results from attack by a minute sap sucking insect, the felted beech coccus, followed by infection by a parasitic fungus, *Nectria coccinea*. The combined attack of insect and fungus can lead to the death of the tree from moisture stress.

7.4.4   Timber properties

Beech is a diffuse porous wood; its pores are small and are spread uniformly throughout the wood. This feature and the absence of large rays or pronounced grain give beech excellent woodworking properties. It is widely used in cabinet making, high-class joinery, solid and laminated furniture, desks and chairs, parquet flooring and plywood. The average density of the wood at 15% moisture content is about 720 kg/m^3.

The wood is easily bent to form new shapes after steam treatment and this process is widely used in the manufacture of bentwood chairs. High quality logs can be rotary peeled to give a serviceable veneer which is used in beech faced plywood and medium density fibreboard. Alternatively, sliced veneer from the radial surface shows an attractive ray feature that is much more decorative. Beech makes excellent floor-blocks. It is the most widely used wood in the furniture industry, much of it out of sight in framing upholstery or as a base for more decorative veneer. Although it is often used for tool handles its short fibres, which confer poor elasticity and brittleness attributes, make it inferior to ash for this purpose.

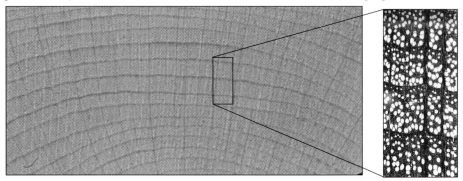

Cross section of beech   **X 40**

On the Continent beech, because of the facility with which it takes stains and its diffuse porous structure, is now regarded as the temperate species most likely to substitute for the decreasing supply of tropical hardwoods.

When freshly cut the wood is white but takes on a pinkish or reddish brown colour with age. There is no clear distinction between heartwood and sapwood. Some trees show a reddish centre that may be mistaken for heartwood but this is a defect known as red heart. It is thought to be age related but site conditions such as the moisture regime and high pH are probably contributory factors. Red heart usually occurs between 100 and 120 years into the rotation and, although it does not significantly affect strength properties, it is a degrade to the extent that it reduces the price of the product by half in Denmark, and even more in Germany.

Beech has little natural resistance to decay, especially if it is in contact with water. However, the timber is permeable to preservative treatment, which gives it excellent durability (railway sleepers for example).

7.5 PRODUCTION GOALS

The objective should be to produce material of high quality and of a size suitable for veneer and furniture manufacturing. This will involve the production of straight, cylindrical, branch-free boles, 8 m or more in length and of a diameter 50 - 60 cm at mid-point. With rapid growth this objective should be achieved over a rotation of 100 - 120 years depending on yield class. Such a rotation will help to reduce the risk of red heart occurrence.

7.6 STAND ESTABLISHMENT

7.6.1 Site preparation

7.6.1.1 *Fencing (see Section 2.3.1.1)*

7.6.1.2 *Vegetation control and soil preparation (see Section 2.3.1.2)*

7.6.2 Regeneration of old woodland

7.6.2.1 *Natural regeneration*

Beech is especially well adapted to natural regeneration under the uniform shelterwood system. As a shade bearer its preferred environment in youth is one of partial shade, protected from frost and desiccating winds, and free of competition from grass and weeds. Such conditions are best obtained by regenerating from seed under cover of the existing stand. This will ensure a favourable microclimate and, when the regeneration operation coincides with a mast year, seedling densities that will provide an adequate quota of stems for selection of quality trees.

Stands suitable for natural regeneration should have trees of acceptable height growth for their age and a low level of forking and spiral growth. Good seed years occur at intervals of 5 -15 years. Preparation of the stand for seeding involves removal of some trees to allow just sufficient light to reach the forest floor. Beech seedlings can tolerate a good deal of shade, and too much light may allow ash and sycamore to dominate in the regeneration and enable weed growth to flourish.

When a decision is made to regenerate, the forest floor is treated in summer with glyphosate to control weed growth. Then in the autumn the soil is rotovated twice, once before and once after seed fall (see Section 2.3.1.2.1).

A schematic representation of the modified uniform shelterwood system and a general outline of the stages involved are presented below (Figure 7.4).

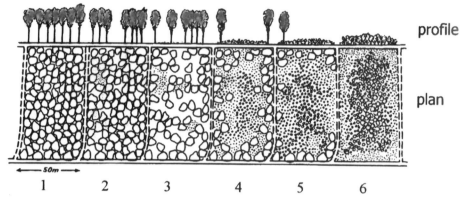

Figure 7.4: Schematic representation of the modified uniform shelterwood system (from Burschel and Huss, 1997)

The modified uniform shelterwood system entails:

1. the presence of a mature fully stocked closed stand at the regeneration stage;
2. preparatory felling: a cautious opening of the canopy through removal of some 15% of standing volume; this is mainly to encourage litter breakdown;
3. seeding felling: in mast year remove 30 - 40% of the standing volume; this operation takes place generally after seed fall;
4. removal fellings: beginning in the centre area between two racks, the shelter of the old stand is gradually removed - the number of interventions depends on the development of the seedlings and the needs of management; this operation can last from 8 - 20 years; the modified system presents an opportunity to introduce mixtures through enrichment planting;
5. final felling: the remainder of the old crop is removed, concentrating on the margins: trees along the extraction paths, which do not present a danger to the young trees, may be retained longer;
6. the mostly even aged and uniform young growth replaces the old crop.

The aim is to keep the young crop growing well. Removal fellings should be directed to the development of the seedlings. If the growth tends to deflect towards the horizontal the shade is too dense and removal of some overstorey trees is needed. However, heavy abrupt fellings should be avoided as young beech prefer partial shade. Furthermore, it is important to retain the mother trees for shelter and seed bearing; this is particularly important when regeneration is sparse or sporadic. Finally, the removal of the old crop must be done with care. Felling of a large beech tree destroys the newly regenerated crop over the area covered by the fallen crown. The idea is to ensure that as many trees as possible fall onto the one place, thus keeping damage to a minimum. This demands careful felling. The small areas of young growth damaged during felling can either be planted with other species to provide a mixture or, if the plants are large enough, they can be cut back to 5 - 10 cm above ground to allow sprouting (see Section 7.4.1.1).

Natural regeneration is sometimes regarded with mixed feelings. This is particularly so with pioneer species, such as birch, and with conifers, such as Sitka spruce. Sporadic regeneration or its failure to materialise can give rise to delay in establishment, while overabundance can lead to costly respacing. In such situations the forester will often opt for artificial regeneration as being the least problematic.

Forty-year old naturally regenerated beech stand in Northrhine, Westphalia

Natural regeneration of beech (one year old) by the uniform shelterwood system, Randhol Forest District, Denmark

With beech, however, there is no necessity to respace. The young plants will compete with each other and crown differentiation will take place naturally. Only the wolves need to be removed before the thicket stage (see Section 7.8). Therefore, natural regeneration should always be the first choice if the option is available, because the canopy of the old stand provides shelter for the young plants against exposure and frost. In addition, the competition provided ensures smaller branches and a high degree of natural pruning, a much better selection of quality trees and ultimately a better quality of final crop trees.

In times of nursery stock scarcity, natural regeneration provides a reservoir from which plants can be supplied. Patches of dense seedlings provide the opportunity to collect wildings (which should be less than 1 m in height), which can be used to fill-in those areas that are less densely stocked. Alternatively, wildings can be used for enrichment planting in stands where there are no beech mother trees or seed bearers.

7.6.3 Afforestation

7.6.3.1 *Artificial regeneration*

Planting broadleaves is an expensive operation, so it should be undertaken with care using healthy plants with a good root/shoot ratio. Forest Service and British Standard nursery stock specifications are shown in Table 7.4. On the Continent two year old undercut seedlings are frequently used on vegetation-free ground.

Table 7.4: Recommended sizes for bare-rooted beech transplants

Organisation	Maximum age	Minimum root collar diameter	Maximum root collar diameter	Minimum height	Maximum height
	years	mm	mm	cm	cm
Forest Service	3	5	-	20	40
	4	6	-	40	55
	4	7	-	55	70
	5	9	-	70	85
	-	11	-	85	85 +
British Standards Institute	-	4	7.5	20	50

Wildings can be used to supplement plant supply. However, they should never be planted into open ground, only under the shelter of existing stands. They are especially suitable for underplanting procedures. They can be used for afforestation, especially if collected from registered seed stands, only after at least one year transplanting in a nursery.

Beech is generally regarded as the most sensitive of the broadleaves in its ability to withstand rough handling prior to planting (see Section 2.3.2).

Since beech should not be planted on wet ground mounding will not be necessary.

7.6.3.1.1 *Pure beech crops*

Sites suitable for pure beech should not be prone to late frosts or subject to undue exposure. Such sites are often found on valley slopes near the coast or on sheltered slopes of low hills in the Midlands. Preferably they should have some tree cover; old woodland sites are ideal provided the soil is suitable for beech. On such sites a light cover is maintained if there is danger from frost. Where frost is not a problem such woodland lends itself to artificial regeneration by the group method in which openings (1/3 - 1/2 ha) are created and planted. The surrounding woodland provides for adequate side shelter.

In Denmark 6,000 plants/ha is considered to be the minimum requirement for planting pure beech. In Germany, 6,000 - 10,000 plants/ha are regarded as necessary if they are not sheltered by an overstorey. This close spacing ensures that trees will grow upward rather than spread outwards. Furthermore, because of the higher stand density they will develop light branches, which will gradually be shaded out and killed as the stand develops and, because of their small diameter, will be more readily shed. This leads to a greater opportunity for selection of trees with straight stems and branch free boles, an essential requirement for quality timber.

Given sufficient growing space beech has a tendency to adopt a coarse habit of growth. To curb this tendency it should be established in close formation, either pure or in mixture with other species.

For pure plantations it is recommended to plant 6,600 plants/ha, in lines 2 m apart and 0.75 m in the lines.

Pure stands of beech are much more costly to establish than mixtures but, provided site conditions are suitable, they tend to be easier to manage in the formative stage.

7.6.3.1.2 *Beech mixtures with conifers*

Mixtures, particularly beech/conifer mixtures, although less costly to establish, often need a greater management expertise to ensure that the conifers do not dominate in the early years. Mixtures, however, often are an essential component to provide a degree of shelter from exposure and frost on open windswept sites. Depending on the management and silvicultural objectives, beech/conifer mixtures can be regarded as nursing or permanent mixtures. The two, however, are not mutually exclusive in that nursing mixtures can be adapted to permanent mixtures, later in the rotation, by retaining suitable conifers (larch or Scots pine) in lines or groups. European or hybrid larches are compatible trees in mixture with beech. They increase the value of the final crop and are independent of rotation length in that the wood does not deteriorate with age.

The two options outlined below provide a framework that can be adapted to suit most situations:

- As stated above (see Section 7.6.2.1) young beech prefer to grow in partial shade and will usually be difficult to establish without the aid of overhead cover on open, exposed areas subject to late spring frost. Such situations require the establishment of a nurse crop in advance and introduction of the beech at a later date.

    The area is first planted with European larch at 2 x 2 m or 2.5 x 2.5 m spacing. When the crop is 10 m in height (at about 15 - 20 years), the plantation is line thinned, by removing every second line, reducing the stocking to 1,000 - 1,200 stems/ha. Beech is then introduced in the lines vacated by the larch, under the remaining larch canopy, at a stocking density of 2,000 - 2,500 stems/ha, by planting at 1 m spacing in lines. The larch provides a nursing role. This option has silvicultural merit in that the beech will be established more rapidly in the favourable microclimate created by the larch. However, it requires greater management expertise to ensure the larch does not dominate. Gradual and judicious removal of larch will be required. Some of the best, well-formed larch may, however, be retained.

- The second option is suited to situations not prone to late spring frost where a more suitable microclimate and side shelter from exposure is provided by a mixture of beech with European or hybrid larch. This option involves planting two (or three) lines of beech at 2 x 0.75 m spacing, alternating with one line of larch at 2 x 2 m spacing. If there is any danger from late spring frost, planting lines should be oriented N - S provide protection from the early morning sun. The larch also provides side shelter in the early years and performs the role of nurse to the beech. If so desired, and the larch are of good quality, this nursing mixture can be converted to a permanent one. Some well developed larch, with good crowns and straight stems, may be high pruned and allowed to grow to the full beech rotation. They will need to be relieved from crown competition by the beech in the second half of the rotation.

On poorer sites Scots pine should be substituted for the larch.

Apart from differences in planting configuration and a greater proportion of beech in the mixture, this is similar to the option under which most of the existing stands of beech in Ireland were established in the 1930s and 1940s.

7.6.3.1.3 *Beech mixtures with other broadleaves*

Mixtures with other broadleaved species need to take into account their relative rotation lengths. Species with longer rotations are the oaks; those with shorter rotations are ash, cherry and sycamore.

Planting intimate mixtures of beech and oak together is rarely satisfactory. Beech has a tendency to outgrow the oak at 80 - 100 years and eventually assume dominance. Where beech/oak mixtures are required it is preferable to plant the oak in groups of a minimum size of 100 m². Problems in reconciling the differing rotation lengths for beech and oak may also arise. After felling of the main beech crop, the oak will need an understorey if development of epicormic branches is to be avoided.

Most beech plantations have a component of single stems of self-sown ash. This should be retained provided it does not exceed one third of the total crop or it is not located in such a fashion that it will create large openings in the canopy structure when harvested at 60 - 80 years. On suitable sites ash will outgrow the beech and maintain dominance until harvested.

Sycamore grows well in mixture with beech. Unlike ash, the quality of its wood does not deteriorate with age, and it can be retained for the full beech rotation. However, beech has a tendency to outgrow and suppress sycamore during the second half of the rotation. For this reason group mixtures of sycamore, of a minimum area of 100 m², are preferable to line mixtures and are more easily managed. Naturally regenerated wild cherry should always be favoured. Rotations for wild cherry are similar to those for ash.

7.6.4 Vegetation management

Competition from grass and weeds is a major problem in all young beech crops. On open ground, beech has neither the vigour of ash and sycamore nor the resilience of the oaks to cope with competition from briars and weeds. Vegetation control is therefore an essential operation and should be carried out until the plants are no longer threatened by competition from the vegetation (see Section 2.3.5).

7.7 FORMATIVE SHAPING

Beech is regarded as a species lacking in apical dominance with a strong propensity to coarse growth. Without formative shaping the species has a tendency to produce trees lacking in the attributes needed for quality timber production (see Section 2.3.6).

7.8   TENDING (See also section 2.3.7)

In naturally regenerated beech stands, seedling densities can be in excess of 100,000 plants/ha. By the time the crop has reached the tending stage (5 - 8 m in height), natural mortality will ensure that only a proportion of these has survived. At this stage, local site differences and genetic variation will have forced the crop to differentiate into the height classes of dominants, co-dominants, sub-dominants and suppressed. For purposes of tending the sub-dominant and suppressed trees can be ignored. Only the dominants and co-dominants are of concern.

The tending operation should remove the coarse branched, forked and deformed stems among the dominants and co-dominants, and ensure the survival and continued development of about 1,000 potential final crop trees/ha. It is recommended that the operation be undertaken when the crop reaches a top height of 5 - 8 m.

In pure beech crops, planted at 6,600 plants/ha, the tending operation should also take place at 5 - 8 m top height.

The same general principles also apply in situations where the beech has been introduced into pole stage larch, but the role of the larch should be defined (see Section 7.6.3.1.2).

If the function of the larch is to provide a nursing role for the beech the larch crop will be removed gradually as its nursing role diminishes, apart from some selected larch which may be retained for the entire rotation.

If the larch is intended as a permanent mixture it will be retained with the beech.

A similar approach should be adopted where beech has been planted in lines alternating with a line of larch (see Section 7.6.3.1.2). Larch will outgrow beech in the early years and vigilance will be required to ensure that it does not dominate the beech. If its role in the mixture is one of nurse, any tendency towards suppression of the beech should be dealt with by removal of the larch even at an early stage. By the time the beech reaches the thinning stage (height 12-14 m) all the larch will have been removed, unless a decision is made to retain selected stems for the full rotation. These should be pruned to 6 m (see Section 2.3.8).

Although tending will be a loss making operation, it is the most effective procedure to ensure a good economic outcome for the final crop.

7.9   PRUNING

Pruning of beech is not generally recommended. Pruning scars do not occlude quickly without rapid diameter growth and present a danger of infection by fungi. With good silvicultural management effective self-pruning should be achieved up to 8 m at 35 - 40 years (see Section 2.3.8).

7.10   THINNING

Thinning of beech commences at 12 - 15 m top height (estimated at 35 - 40 years depending on site) in the form of a selective crown thinning to promote the continued development of 150 potential final crop trees. Beech, with its diffuse porous wood structure, improves in quality with rapid growth, provided this growth is uniform.

However, too rapid release of the mostly large crowned trees may lead to epicormic branch development. This situation should be avoided but within this limit, the more rapid the growth the better the timber quality.

Selection of the final crop trees should follow the procedure outlined in Section 2.3.9.

Special care should be taken during thinning and extraction to avoid damage to the final crop trees. Beech, with its thin bark, is extremely susceptible to bark damage, which provides an entry for decay fungi and leads to heart rot.

In concentrating on the final crop trees the remainder of the stand should not be ignored. Promising beech trees of good form in the pockets between the final crop trees, (and especially self-sown wild cherry, ash, sycamore and oak) which will be retained for part of the rotation, should also be released. They act as reserves in case the final crop trees suffer damage or become forked. The middle storey, and particularly the understorey, must be largely retained to control development of epicormic branching on the final crop stems and provide ground cover.

In beech, thinning proceeds up to an age 20 years before the end of the rotation.

A rough rule-of-thumb for determining the interval in years between successive thinnings (thinning cycle) is obtained by dividing the age of the crop by 10; a 40-year old crop will be thinned every four years; a 50-year old crop every 5 years, and so on. This rule caters to some extent for the decrease in current height increment as the stand grows older.

Oak

Pedunculate oak *Quercus robur L.*
Dair Ghallda
Sessile oak *Quercus petraea L.*
Dair Ghaelach

Oak, 250 years old with beech understorey, Johanniskreuz, Rheinland - Pfalz, German

8.1. Summary

Oak timber is widely used for furniture manufacture and joinery where strength and durability are required. High quality logs are in demand for veneer, to decorate less attractive woods and to provide a stable medium in centrally heated environments. High quality veneer logs command the best price of all the broadleaves, even wild cherry, but these are unlikely to exceed 20% by volume of the best oak stands.

The oaks (pedunculate and sessile) are accommodating in regard to site, with pedunculate oak occupying the heavier soils of the lowlands and sessile growing on the lighter soils of the hills and uplands. However, the optima for both species are deep, fertile, fine textured, slightly acid soils in those locations. Pedunculate oak, with its strong taproot, is the only species with the capacity to penetrate heavy gley soils. The deep rooting habit of both species makes them extremely windfirm.

Oak is intolerant of shade and will stagnate if the crown is not provided with sufficient light. It is the most difficult of the broadleaves to grow successfully because of the production of epicormic branching. Without a suitable understorey to protect the stems from light the production of high quality veneer trees will not be possible. Estimated economic rotations are 130 years for pedunculate and 160 years for sessile.

8.1.1 Key Characteristics

- Strong light demander
- Accommodating in regard to site
- Susceptible to late spring and early autumn frost
- Excellent stability to wind
- Susceptible to damage by grey squirrel
- Medium ability for natural pruning
- Prone to development of epicormic branches
- Susceptible to shake

8.1.2 General silvicultural treatment for oak

Top height m	Stocking after treatment trees/ha	Comment
0.2- 1.0	6,600	Planted at 2.0 x 0.75 m (2 m between rows).
2-3	6,000	Formative shaping - singling of forked leaders.
4 - 5	5,000	2nd formative shaping (if necessary).
6 - 7	3,600	Tending - remove wolves, crooked and badly forked stems. In oak/conifer mixtures remove dominating European larch or Scots pine.
10 - 11	1,900 - 2,100	2nd tending (if necessary) - in oak/conifer mixtures remove conifers.
13 - 15	1,000 - 1,300	Crown thinning. Select about 100 final crop trees/ha. Underplant with beech or hornbeam.
15 - 30		Thin to remove competitors (2 - 3 stems/final crop tree) at intervals of 1.5 - 2 m height growth.
30 - 33	90 - 110	Fell crop at 65 - 70 cm breast height diameter.

8.2 NATURAL DISTRIBUTION AND OCCURRENCE

The pedunculate and sessile oaks (*Quercus robur* and *Quercus petraea*) colonised Europe soon after the ice sheets receded. In the 'oak-mixture period' they covered the warm lowlands and extended much higher into the mountains than they do today. However, because the pollen of the two species is indistinguishable it is now impossible to determine the extent of their respective distributions at that time. As the climate became colder and more humid they were partly displaced by the invading beech and retreated to sites less favoured by beech about 2000 BP. In central Europe, at least, it must be assumed that the oaks were propagated by man, so their distribution has been subjected to more human influence than any other species.

Today the oaks extend through most of Europe from Scandinavia to the Mediterranean and from the Atlantic through Asia Minor to the Caspian Sea. Their distribution limits are, however, very different and throughout Europe pedunculate oak is more a tree of the plains and foothills with a slight preference for a continental climate. It is understandable, therefore, that pedunculate stretches far into the east of Europe (Figure 8.1).

Figure 8.1: Natural distribution of pedunculate oak

In contrast, sessile oak has a much smaller natural distribution, being concentrated mainly in the more sub-atlantic regions (Figure 8.2), where its climatic requirements resemble those of the beech.

Figure 8.2: Natural distribution of sessile oak

Here it inhabits the hills and lower mountain ranges and can rightfully be regarded as 'the oak of the mountains'.

In Ireland, oak is irrevocably linked to the ancient woodlands and the number of place names with 'derry' point to its widespread distribution. It was extensively exploited over the centuries but trees of exceptional quality seem to have still remained into the 15th century.

Samuel Hayes, writing in 1794, comments that "Tradition gives the *Shillela Oak* the honor (sic) of roofing Westminster-Hall and other buildings of that age; the timbers which support the leads of the magnificent Chapel of King's College, Cambridge, which was built in 1444, as also the roof of Henry the Eight's chapel in Westminster-Abbey, are said to be oak brought from these woods, ...".

Following exploitation of the high forest the woods were managed on a coppice or coppice-with-standards system for centuries. Many of the oak woods of Wicklow are remnants of these coppice woods, which have again reverted to high forest. During the 18th century estate planting with oak was common but these matured only to be decimated for timber supplies during two World Wars. With few exceptions little by way of reconstitution took place and the unwanted culls have matured to form gnarled old trees with heavy branches and poor stem quality. Although such trees are of little commercial value they are often highly regarded from an aesthetic viewpoint by recreationists and by conservationists.

Oak seems to have been regarded as a site demanding species and younger plantations are consequently relatively few. It is however apparent that foresters recognised the need for reasonably high stocking densities and such plantations as exist were invariably established in 50/50 mixture with European larch or Scots pine, at densities of 5,300 or 6,600/ha. The conifer component provided a nursing role and was gradually removed as this function was completed. Today the area of state woodland with oak as principal species is just over 4,000 ha, approximately 25% of all broadleaved species. A limited survey of these woodlands showed oak growing well over a wide range of soil types.

Remnants of the once extensive oak forest of Wicklow and north Wexford still remain in Avonmore, Coolgreaney, Glendalough and Glenealy forests. Oak is found growing successfully on the drumlins of Monaghan and Cavan and its performance on heavy gley can be seen in locations as far apart as Dartrey, near Cootehill, Co Cavan and Dromdeer, south of Doneraile, Co Cork. It has reached sizeable dimensions on free-draining old red sandstone soils, in south Kerry and the Slieve Aughty range in Clare and south-east Galway. One of the best young stands in the country (planted 1935) was established in a 50/50 mixture with European larch at Kilcooly, Callan forest, Co Tipperary.

8.3   PROVENANCE

Quercus petraea and *Q. robur* are both native species. In past times they constituted a significant part of the native woodland, which covered a large part of the land area of this country. Today only a very small area of this (ancient) native woodland survives. All of this woodland has been influenced by man's activities at some stage. Coppicing, selective felling, clearfelling and the grazing of seedlings by domestic stock have played a significant role in reducing the once extensive area of oak forests in this country. Inevitably the native oak population has been severely depleted both in size and possibly genetic constitution. Large-scale clearfellings for agriculture and selective fellings of good phenotypes in closed stands, which did not allow regeneration to take place, may have resulted in the loss of many valuable genotypes. Where coppicing was practised, however, the genetic diversity of stands would have been maintained since this method of propagation relies on the vegetative renewal of a stand from cut stumps.

Until recently most of the seed used in establishing oak plantations in Ireland was of home collected origin. In past centuries private landowners would have used seed collected from existing stands on their estates. How much and to what extent this practice occurred is unknown. In the state forests, however, the National Tree Seed Register shows that during a 50-year period, from the start of the state afforestation programme in the late 1920s to 1980, 25% of oak seed was imported, mostly from Germany and the Netherlands. In recent years the rapid increase in the national afforestation programme and the attractive incentives for planting broadleaves have resulted in the demand for seed and plants far exceeding supply from Irish nurseries. These factors, coupled with a lack of good mast years and the difficulties involved in storing acorns for more than half a year, have inevitably resulted in the importation of large quantities of acorns and plants.

Information on provenance variation in oak is very limited. Studies indicate that both species hybridise fairly freely but the tendency is for oak in the hills to have more of the *Quercus petraea* characteristics. Good stands of continental sources have been identified and are clearly suitable for growing in Ireland. How these perform relative to native material is not known at present. Provenance trials were established in the late 1980s testing a range of native and foreign origins. Information on early growth and adaptability is becoming available but volume production and quality traits will not be fully expressed until the trials are at least one third of their rotation length (about 40 years). In the interim period, material from registered Irish stands should be a first choice. However, if seed and plants must be imported then it is recommended that material should come from registered seed stands growing in the UK, Netherlands, Belgium and the northern parts of France and Germany - regions which have a climate not too dissimilar to Ireland. Central and south-eastern European sources are not recommended until their suitability has been determined in field trials.

8.4 ECOLOGICAL DEMANDS AND CHARACTERISTICS OF THE SPECIES

8.4.1 Biology, morphology, autecology and growth performance

8.4.1.1 *Biology and morphology*

Of the two oaks, pedunculate forms the more impressive tree, reaching heights up to 40 m although 30 m is more the norm. It may grow to more than 2 m in diameter and may well exceed 500 years of age.

The crown of pedunculate oak fades into big, often crooked branches, whereas that of sessile usually keeps a straight monopodial structure, although attaining less imposing dimensions. There are great variations in shape between different provenances, which often outweigh those between the species.

Both species show a specific root system, with a definite taproot often penetrating to a depth of 2 m in youth. Later in life the root system develops into a heart-shaped form. Oaks have the most intensive root systems of all broadleaved species, especially on heavy soils. On that account they are exceptionally windfirm although, on occasions when in full leaf, they may be windthrown by a combination of summer gales and high precipitation.

Both oak species have a good ability to sprout from stools. The oaks have therefore been widely used in the coppice silvicultural system since early times and it is still an important feature of French and Italian forests. Sprouting potential declines gradually with age and volume production decreases after a number of coppice rotations. However, reliable data are unavailable.

Leaves are set alternately, usually with a pair of auricles at the base for pedunculate and a more tapered (cuneate) base for sessile. Pedunculate oak acorns are carried on a peduncle 4 - 8 cm long; those of sessile oak are sessile or on a peduncle up to 1 cm long. Their respective names are derived from those features. However, there is a wide range of variation in both species and they tend to hybridise.

Pedunculate oak　　　　　　　　　　　　　**Sessile oak**

Both species are very susceptible to late spring frost. However, they avoid frost damage in normal years by flushing in late April/May, after beech. Sessile oak begins growth earlier in spring but is damaged less often because it normally grows in hilly terrain where late frost is less frequent and not as severe as in the lowlands. There is some anecdotal evidence that pedunculate oak may flush earlier at certain sites. Both oaks show a strong tendency towards lammas growth in June/July and this may help to compensate for loss in height growth during spring (from frost and insect damage). In warm summers a second and even a third flushing in August is possible. Very often the latter may not be sufficiently hardened-off before the onset of frost and this can lead to terminal bud damage and forking.

There are large differences between provenances and even individuals in regard to the development of epicormic branches. Compared to the Continent, oak in Ireland seems to be especially susceptible to epicormic growth.

Flowers are monoecious, usually producing acorns singly on pedunculate and in clusters on sessile oak. The flowers appear at time of leaf flushing and are wind pollinated. Oak acorns are among the heaviest fruits of all native European trees; 1,000 acorns weigh 2,000 - 3,500 g. The acorns ripen in October and are able to produce a radicle immediately (but not a shoot, which must await a period of winter chilling). However, they very soon lose this capacity. This makes it difficult to store acorns for longer than a few months without employing special handling measures. This is one of the reasons why central European foresters tend to sow acorns immediately after collection. In the nursery, sowing is usually done in March after soaking in water for 48 hours to return the moisture content to the desired level.

Flowering starts relatively late, at an age of 20 - 30 years, for isolated trees and much later, after 50 years, in stands. Fructification is very uncertain. Mast years occur at intervals of 5 - 10 years and are obviously, like beech, dependent on the weather conditions in late summer of the previous year. Even when flowers form they may be damaged by late frost or by insect attack.

8.4.1.2   *Seed collection and storage*

For storing over the winter, acorns are harvested from the ground in October and, because of their high moisture content, should be spread out in a cool aerated place to a depth not exceeding 10 cm. They are turned and mixed frequently to allow the moisture content to decrease uniformly and prevent heating. The desired moisture content for winter storage is 42 to 48%.

Acorns can be stored for up to 2 years at - 3°C if they are soaked for two to three hours in water maintained at a temperature of 41°C before storage. This is necessary to protect against the fungus *Ciboria batchiana*, which causes blackening of the acorns.

8.4.1.3   *Autecology*

As already stated both species have a wide climatic range and need sufficient summer warmth for good growth. Pedunculate oak tolerates more continentally influenced conditions, whereas sessile prefers oceanic climates. Thus pedunculate is less susceptible to damage by deep winter frost.

Pedunculate oak is very accommodating in regard to site and grows on acid soils as well as on very basic ones. It prefers sites well supplied with water but is also able to grow on very dry soils. It can tolerate flooding for long periods and is a frequent constituent of riverine forests.

Sessile oak is also tolerant of all soils regardless of their pH-status. Its ability to withstand dry conditions is even better than pedunculate but its tolerance of wet soils is much less.

Both species are relatively indifferent to geological substrate and nutrient status although, like most European tree species, they show their best growth on well drained and fertile soils.

Because of its better ability to grow on heavy soils, like surface-water gleys and pelosols, pedunculate oak is even found on very compact soil, whereas sessile oak is limited to more sandy soils.

Both species are light demanders. Sessile oak, however, tolerates more shade up to the thicket stage. It can survive for longer periods underneath the shelter of old trees but this usually results in poor growth and crooked stems.

8.4.1.4   *Growth performance*

Like all light demanding tree species the oaks show a rapid height growth in the early years. However, cumulative height growth is impressive only on the very best sites. According to German yield models for very good sites the oaks reach 31 m at 100 years and 40 m at 200 years (Figure 8.4). Comparison with poorer sites shows that the differences in height growth occur during the first 30 years. British models show slightly lower height (30 m) at 100 years and reach only 33 m at 150 years. Both pedunculate and sessile oaks are thought to follow similar growth patterns in Germany and in Britain so one yield model caters for both species in each country. French tables indicate much more rapid growth rates for pedunculate with a dominant height of 35 m at 100 years compared to 30 m for sessile at the same age. Recommended rotation lengths in France are also markedly different for the two species, ranging from 100 to 140 years for pedunculate and 170 to 200 years for sessile according to yield class. This, however, may well be a reflection of the more fertile soils selected for pedunculate oak.

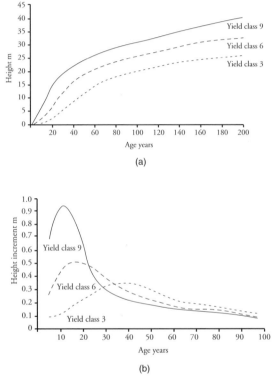

Figure 8.4: (a) Cumulative height growth of oak for yield classes 3, 6, and 9, (b) height increment of the same yield classes (from German yield table, Jüttner, 1955)

In Germany current annual height increment culminates between 10 and 20 years for the best yield classes (yield class 9) and later than 30 years on poor sites (yield class 3). British yield models indicate a culmination of height increment at about 30 and 40 years respectively for the best (yield class 8) and poorest (yield class 4) classes, while French models for sessile oak are intermediate. All, however, show the same trend with later culmination of height increment for the poorer yield classes.

Table 8.1 shows the number of trees/ha, basal area/ha, standing volume/ha and mean diameter for different ages and yield classes in German and British yield models.

Table 8.1: Growth data for oak of different yield classes, in Britian and Germany

Parameter	Age	Yield Class m³/ha/year					
		British	German	British	German	British	German
	years	8	9	6	6	4	3
Stocking trees/ha	30	1,479	2,130	2,144	3,732	3,750	7,325
	100	111	229	156	300	244	642
	150	52	103	78	129	123	264
	200		59		75		228
Basal area m²/ha	100	23.7	27.1	23.4	25.1	22.8	23.0
	150	20.6	28.2	21.6	25.8	21.7	23.8
	200		29.7		26.7		23.7
Standing volume m³/ha	100	306	431	261	326	202	214
	150	298	522	268	411	211	288
	200		609[1]		469		297
Mean dbh cm	100	52.2	39.0	43.6	33.0	34.5	21.0
	150	71.3	59.0	59.3	50.0	47.4	34.0
	200		80.0		67.0		36.0

In central Europe the number of trees/ha continues to be relatively high as most of the stands were, and still are, established by artificial seeding of acorns in Germany or by natural regeneration in France. Only in recent times has the proportion of planted stands increased. For plantations the number of plants/ha usually varies, according to plant size and quality, between 5,000 and 10,000/ha, but the tendency is to reduce this number and use tall, sturdy plants up to 2.5 m in height. The data give an idea of continental practice in relation to crop characteristics and yield class. British yield models show a stocking density of about 5,000 trees/ha at 20 years of age (the first entry in the tables) suggesting that the initial stocking was of the order of 6,000 or more trees/ha.

Basal area/ha varies little between yield classes in British tables but there is an upward trend with increasing yield class and age in the German models.

The development pattern of standing volume/ha in British models shows a moderate increase with yield class but remains constant (or even decreases slightly) between the ages of 100 - 150 years. German models also indicate an increase in volume/ha with higher yield class but in contrast to the British model show an increase with age. In effect standing volume/ha increases by around 50% between ages 100 and 200 years.

As one might expect mean diameters at breast height increase with higher yield class for both the British and German models. However, for a common age of 100 years the mean diameters in the British model are substantially larger for comparable yield classes. An even more pertinent statistic is that it takes 150 years in the British model and 200 years in the German model to attain the target diameter specified in the production objectives (see Section 8.5), and then only for the highest yield classes.

Analysis of the data in the above table indicates that the main differences between the British and German models are due to the type of thinning employed. The conventional thinning type for broadleaves in Britian has been a heavy crown thinning; this promotes diameter growth at the expense of standing volume/ha. The oak stands used to construct the German

[1] For older stand on exceptionally good sites

yield models, however, were thinned conventionally employing light, low thinning. This increases standing volume/ha substantially but at the expense of diameter growth.

Modern thinning concepts on the Continent are now oriented towards intensive crown thinning in order to improve diameter growth (see Section 8.10).

Notwithstanding the mystique associated with growing oak in Ireland it must be concluded that the growing of commercial oak can be justified only on good sites and that the production of quality timber is imperative.

Oak management inevitably involves long rotations. Taking into account the long pay back period this may well make commercial oak production less attractive to small forest owners.

In Germany, oak stands are found only in the public forests and on a few large private estates.

8.4.2   Site requirements

The optimum soil conditions for the oaks are deep, fertile acidic fine-textured soils but they have the capacity to accommodate themselves to a wide range of soil types.

Pedunculate oak is usually associated with the heavy clay soils of the lowlands while sessile grows on the freer draining, less fertile soils of the hills. Their best growth, however, is on deep, acid brown earths on sheltered sites in these locations.

However, in contrast to the other broadleaved species considered (ash, beech, sycamore and wild cherry), oak is relatively indifferent to site conditions. Good, or at least moderate, growth of oak was recorded in the soil studies on most of the major soils throughout the country, ranging through the upland podzols and brown podzolics to the lowland brown earths, grey brown podzolics, and gleys.

The unique capacity of oak to grow so successfully on such a wide range of conditions is illustrated by reference to some examples from the soil investigations at the oak stands (Table 8.2).

Table 8.2: Sites found suitable for the growth of oak

Soil	Property	Forest	Dominant Parent Material	Soil pH (top to bottom of soil profile)
Podzol	Glengarra Wood	Galtee	Old red sandstone	4.3-5.4
Podzol	Doon	Broadford	Old red sandstone	4.0-4.7
Podzol	Glenhouse	Curraghmore	Old red sandstone	4.2-4.5
Brown podzolic	Stafford Avenue	Avonmore	Shale	4.0-4.4
Brown podzolic	Ballyfad	Coolgreaney	Shale	4.4-4.5
Brown podzolic	Ballard	Glendalough	Shale	4.0-4.8
Brown podzolic	Laragh	Glendalough	Granite	3.9-4.7
Brown podzolic	Ballymanus	Glenealy	Shale	3.8-4.8
Grey brown podzolic	Aghrane	Ballygar	Limestone	6.6-7.5
Grey brown podzolic	Kilcooly	Callan	Limestone	6.8-8.2
Grey brown podzolic	Monarche	Callan	Limestone	5.2-7.4
Grey brown podzolic	Dunmore	Castlecomer	Limestone	5.6-8.2
Grey brown podzolic	Demesne	Mountbellew	Limestone	5.1-8.2
Gley	Dartrey	Monaghan	Sandstone	4.2-6.8
Gley	Dromdeer	Killavullen	Sandstone	5.4-5.0

Notwithstanding the remarkable tolerance of oak to the varying soil conditions noted in Table 8.2 above, a few points are worth noting:

1. As regards the gleys, it was noteworthy from the soil investigations that the parent material was composed predominantly of sandstone or sandstone-shale glacial material (with minor inclusions of limestone material or perhaps none). This increases the possibility of at least some drainage, depending on site conditions (particularly slope and runoff characteristics). Such gleys are common in Cavan-Monaghan, especially on the drumlins. The upper and middle slopes of these drumlins can have soils (gleys, gleyed brown earths, and brown earths) with sufficient drainage to sustain good growth of oak, and sometimes even of ash.

   There was no evidence of good oak growth on heavy gley soils - nor would there be that expectation - such as those largely occupying Co Leitrim. These gleys are derived mainly from limestone glacial till, which tends to be a much more tenacious and impermeable material than its sandstone or shale counterparts. Such extreme forms of gley should clearly be avoided for oak, or indeed for any of the main commercial broadleaved species.

2. Whilst oak can grow successfully on most grey brown podzolic soils it would not be the optimum species for that soil type, bearing in mind their limited availability; the preferred species being ash, beech, or sycamore.

3. Oak is reputed to be more vulnerable to shake (a defect manifested by longitudinal or horizontal cracks in the wood) on coarse-textured soils. This tempers enthusiasm for the productive oak stands found on some of the soils, especially the free-draining podzols.

4. The successful growth of oak in Wicklow-Wexford is noteworthy, particularly on soils that are supporting poor ash. These are the acid brown earth and brown podzolic soils developed over glacial till derived from shale parent material.

8.4.3 Post establishment factors affecting growth and development

Both oaks have been generally regarded as the most stable and windfirm of all species of forest trees in Europe and relatively free of damage by pathogens and insect pests. However, in recent years increased damage from pests and diseases have given cause for some concern. An 'oak die-back' spreading from eastern Europe to the west is regarded as a serious threat. This disease is of complex origin but it appears to be caused by climatic extremes combined with secondary infections by fungi. In addition, some cases of complete defoliation have occurred during the past ten years by caterpillars of *Lymantria dispar*.

8.4.3.1 *Abiotic factors*

The deep rooting capacity of both oak species makes them exceptionally windfirm. Nevertheless, as mentioned in section 8.4.1.1 they can occasionally be uprooted by summer gales when combined with high precipitation.

Young oaks retain their dry leaves during winter and in consequence thickets and even pole stage stands can be damaged by snow. On sites susceptible to wet snow single trees or even large stands can suffer severe damage. Old pedunculate oak trees sometimes suffer from snow break because of their weaker branches.

In Europe, pedunculate oak tolerates flooding for up to four months during summer and can grow on soils with a high water-table, such as ground-water gleys, and those with a fluctuating water-table, such as surface-water gleys. In contrast sessile oak can withstand flooding for less than three weeks and wet sites should be avoided.

Pedunculate oak is resistant to winter frost but sessile oak may suffer from frost cracks. Both species are very susceptible to late spring frost. In normal years, however, they avoid damage by flushing relatively late, at the end of April and in May, normally after beech.

As mentioned above (see Section 8.4.1.1) damage by early frost occurs after long and warm late-summer periods which encourage oak to produce lammas shoots a second time (in August). The sudden onset of zero temperatures in autumn can then cause damage to terminal buds which have yet to harden-off. Both types of frost cause forking of leaders in the growing season following the occurrence of damage.

8.4.3.2 *Biotic factors*

Apart from occasional damage by the grey squirrel and the occurrence of oak mildew, the oaks are relatively free of pests and diseases in Ireland. Damage by grey squirrels is much more widespread in Britain, where they do untold damage to oaks. Without good control measures damage is expected to become much more severe in Ireland (see Section 2.3.11).

Stock and rabbit fencing will be necessary to exclude domestic livestock, rabbits and hares, which can cause considerable damage to newly established plantations.

Deer, where present, tend to browse intensively on broadleaves and must be excluded (by deer fencing). With increase in deer populations the growing of oak will become more difficult. Oak acorns are extremely attractive to herbivores, such as deer, and to mice, a factor that must be taken into consideration during natural regeneration, when partial covering of the seed will reduce predation.

Mildew is more serious in the nursery stage; in woodland it is confined almost entirely to coppice shoots and rarely does lasting damage. In continental Europe, and occasionally in Britain, the larvae of the oak leaf roller moth (*Tortrix viridana*) cause defoliation and consequent reduction in volume increment. Frequently, however, the production generated by lammas shoots compensates, at least partially, for this loss.

Of the fungi that attack oak, two are of significance: *Polyporus sulphureus*, causing brown cubical rot and *Stereum gausapatum*, causing pipe rot. These enter the tree through branch stubs in which heartwood has developed. The formation of heartwood in side branches occurs when they exceed 3 cm in diameter at the stem. To avoid infection side branches should not be allowed to develop heartwood. This is best achieved by ensuring that branch diameter is kept small by close spacing. The alternative is early and continuing high pruning.

8.4.4   Timber properties

Oak is a pronounced ring porous wood. Within the annual ring the circles of large vessels which mark the softer, less dense earlywood stand out clearly from the harder, denser latewood. The proportion of earlywood to latewood determines the ease of working and strength properties of the timber. Earlywood width tends to remain constant irrespective of growth rate, so rapidly growing trees will contain a high proportion of latewood relative to earlywood, resulting in high strength properties, greater shrinkage and somewhat poor workability. Conversely, in slow growing trees the ring will consist almost entirely of early wood resulting in poor strength properties, lower shrinkage but good workability. Average density of the wood at 15% moisture content is about 720 kg/m^3.

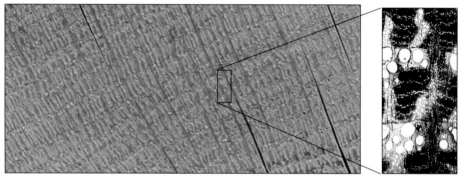

Cross section of oak   **X40**

A distinctive feature of oak timber is the broad rays radiating from the centre of the stem. When sawn radially (quarter-sawn) these show up as large silver coloured plates, giving the ornamental feature known as 'silver grain', which is also a highly valued feature of oak veneer. The wood is normally light tan in colour when freshly cut; it dries slowly and has a tendency to split and check unless care is taken in kiln drying. The heartwood is very durable and resists penetration by preservatives. Sapwood, which is usually confined to the outer 10 to 20 rings in the tree, is perishable but permeable.

Oak timber is used for veneer, furniture manufacture and joinery. High quality veneer logs are mostly of sessile oak origin, although pedunculate oak is sometimes suitable. The determining factors are ring width and uniform growth.   Site factors and species characteristics ensure that sessile oak grows at a much slower rate than pedunculate resulting in average ring widths for sessile of 2 to 2.5 mm compared to 2.5 to 4 mm for pedunculate. Oak is one of the most highly priced timbers for veneer and high quality veneer logs can realise exceptional prices. The criteria for high value oak are:

* a light clear colour;
* straight cylindrical stem;
* concentric rings of uniform growth;
* absolutely blemish-free stems;
* medium dimensions of approximately 60 cm in diameter are specified in Germany (but larger diameters command much higher prices); larger dimensions, 70 cm minimum at breast height (optimum 80 cm), are specified for sessile oak in France.

To meet those criteria management should ensure that the stems are branch free from an early age and that uniform growth is obtained through regular thinning.

One of the major defects in newly felled oak is a condition known as shake. Shake is a longitudinal splitting or separation in the wood, radiating from the centre of the log (star shake) or along the annual ring (ring shake). It extends longitudinally for some distance up the stem and its extent is determined only by cross-cutting. It is a very serious defect causing the timber to split along the shake during processing, thereby reducing the value of what may otherwise be a quality log to that of firewood or fencing material.

The incidence of shake in a stand of oak is difficult to predict before felling, which is one reason why timber merchants prefer to buy oak in the log. Deep fissures or longitudinal ribbing along the stem are usually a sign of 'frost crack' (see Section 8.4.3.1), which occurs occasionally in Ireland but is much more common on the Continent. Studies in Britain have linked the occurrence of shake to trees growing on light, free draining soils but variability between trees on the same site would indicate that there may be some genetic linkage.

More recent work at Oxford University suggests that oak with larger than average sized earlywood vessels are likely to have a greater predisposition to shake. These shake-prone trees can be recognised by their tendency to flush later in springtime.

8.5   PRODUCTION GOALS

The long production period and relatively low final crop volume make it mandatory that oak be grown so as to achieve the greatest possible proportion of veneer and sawtimber assortments. This will ensure the highest value production.

The objectives should be:

- Sessile oak stands with quality veneer potential managed on a 150 to 175 year rotation so as to attain a breast height diameter ranging from 60 to 70 cm;
- Pedunculate oak stands with some veneer potential and a large component of sawlog assortments. On suitable sites this will entail a rotation of 120 to 140 years.

Above: Natural regeneration of oak (5 years) by the uniform shelterwood system, Biebertal, Hessen, Germany
Left: Line of seedlings in direct-sown oak, Spessart, Bavaria, Germany

8.6 STAND ESTABLISHMENT

8.6.1 Site preparation

8.6.1.1 *Fencing*

On most sites, regardless of regeneration method, fencing will be necessary (see Section 2.3.1.1).

8.6.1.2 *Soil preparation*

The growth of crops, regenerated both naturally and artificially, will be considerably improved by soil preparation (see Section 2.3.1.2).

8.6.2 Regeneration of old woodland

8.6.2.1 *Natural regeneration*

Natural regeneration by the uniform shelterwood system (see Section 7.6.2) is the favoured method for renewal of oak stands in France, where some 90% of oak is established in this manner. The procedure for regeneration of the oaks is similar to that outlined for beech (see Sections 7.6.2 and 2.3.1.2.1). With oaks, however, more rapid removal of the overstorey is necessary once regeneration is achieved. Although oak will tolerate some shade in the seedling stage, it needs full light to develop, so the overstorey should not be retained longer than necessary.

Where feasible, natural regeneration (or direct seeding) of oak stands should be preferred to planting. This is more important in the case of oak regeneration than for beech. No deformation of the taproot occurs (as with planting stock) and the root system is stronger and more robust.

8.6.2.2 *Artificial regeneration*

8.6.2.2.1 *Direct Seeding*

Direct seeding is usually associated with regeneration of existing oak stands, when acorns are sown in drills under a light canopy. This method is widely used in Germany, particularly in the Bavarian Spessart and Rheinland-Pfalz regions, for the establishment of sessile oak. The overhead canopy is intended to provide shelter and protection from frost in addition to curbing weed growth. It should be retained for a short period (normally up to 5 years) until the plants are well established.

Variations of the system have been applied in the conversion of tillage land to woodland by sowing acorns with a corn crop and allowing the oak seedlings to grow in the stubble after harvesting the corn. The practice also lends itself to the rehabilitation of degenerated oak woodland or scrubland by retaining a light canopy of tree species (maximum 50% cover) and seeding with acorns.

Direct seeding avoids the nursery stage and the subsequent check which plants experience when transplanted on to the planting site. Unlike conifers, broadleaves are more vigorous in the seedling stage and can grow up to 15 cm in the first year. This attribute makes them more suitable for direct seeding but control of competing vegetation in the early years is essential.

Broadcast seeding with acorns is not considered to be a viable option because of subsequent problems with competing vegetation and other management considerations. The seed-drill approach is more suitable and is the one used. Drills are opened 1.7 - 2 m apart and 5 cm deep. The acorns are sown in the drills at a density of 15 - 20 seeds/m (7 - 5 cm apart), covered with mineral soil and firmed-in. At this density the amount of acorns required will be 400 - 550 kg/ha. In soils with a humus layer it is essential that the seed be placed in the mineral soil.

Sowing should take place in October/November. This avoids the problem of winter storage of the acorns with the associated danger of heating and loss of viability. However, on very wet soils, such as gleys, autumn sowing may lead to the death of the acorns from fungal attack and lack of oxygen. On such soils sowing from January to March during mild weather is more suitable.

In comparison with planting, the main disadvantage of direct seeding arises from competing vegetation. The difficulty in applying chemical vegetation control to seedlings, the longer period of competition, the greater problems in felling and extraction of the residual stand; all point to confining seeding to the drier and less fertile sites where grass and weed growth is not luxuriant. On fertile sites, more suited to pedunculate oak, planting will normally be the favoured option.

8.6.3   Afforestation/Reforestation

8.6.3.1   *Planting*

Planting is the preferred option for afforestation of former tillage land, grassland, wet sites and the conversion of former coniferous woodland to broadleaves (see Section 2.3.1.2).

To avoid losses plants should have a good root/shoot ratio. On the Continent two year old undercut seedlings are frequently used on vegetation free ground. These will usually be 1u1 seedlings or 1+1 transplants. Forest Service and British Standard nursery stock specifications are shown in Table 8.3.

Table 8.3: Recommended sizes for bare-rooted oak transplants

Organisation	Maximum age years	Minimum root collar diameter mm	Maximum root collar diameter mm	Minimum height cm	Maximum height cm
Forest Service	3	5	-	20	40
	4	6	-	40	55
	4	7	-	55	70
	5	9	-	70	85
	-	11	-	85	85 +
British Standards Institute	-	5	9.5	20	50

See Section 2.3.2 for plant handling procedures.

Planting should preferably take place after leaf shed, during mild weather in October/November or, if conditions are not suitable, in early spring.

On the heavier clays and gley soils preference should be given to the pedunculate oak (*Quercus robur*), while sessile oak (*Quercus petraea*) should be planted on the lighter upland soils. However, light drought-prone soils should be avoided because of the risk of shake.

8.6.3.1.1 *Pure oak crops*

Pure crops are more expensive to establish but, in comparison with broadleaved/conifer mixtures, they have the advantage of being less demanding on management expertise up to the thinning stage. Like beech, the oaks are lacking in apical dominance; therefore similar initial stocking densities are recommended. On vegetation-free ground 1u1 or 1+1 plants, 25 - 50 cm in height are most suitable. Where vegetation is likely to give rise to strong competition, older plants (for example 2+1 transplants) 50 - 75 cm in height should be used.

Pure oak should be planted in rows 2.0 m apart and 0.75 m in the row (6,600 plants/ha).

8.6.3.1.2 *Oak mixtures with conifers*

Most oak plantations established in Ireland this century were planted between 1930 and 1950. During the 1930s, establishment of oak groups at 7 m spacing in a matrix of Norway spruce (Anderson groups) was fashionable but practically none of these oak have survived; they were invariably suppressed by the spruce.

Existing stands from this period were planted, almost without exception, at 1.22 m square spacing (6,600 plants/ha) in a 50/50 mixture with European larch, or occasionally with Scots pine or beech. Many of the stands established with European larch show good stem form although branch diameter is greater than desirable. The latter may, however, be due to subsequent silvicultural treatment and/or the absence of an understorey following removal of the larch.

The recommendation is to establish oak in alternate lines with European larch, the lines to be 2 m apart. Oak should be planted at 0.75 m spacing in the lines, giving a quota of 3,300 oak plants/ha. The spacing for the larch should not exceed 2 m in the lines, requiring 1,250 larch/ha. Total plant requirements will therefore be 4,550/ha. The saving in cost is substantial but subsequent management up to the thinning stage will need to be much more intensive to ensure that the oak does not become suppressed. Although oak can show considerable height growth vigour in youth, it is no match for the conifers and care must be taken to ensure that it is not suppressed.

On poorer sites Scots pine may be substituted for larch.

Japanese larch/oak or Norway spruce/oak mixtures should not be used because of the greater danger of suppression of the oak.

Generally the role of the conifers is one of nursing, to provide shelter, curb side branch development and promote height growth. Vigilance will then be required from an early age to ensure that the conifers perform this nursing role and do not at any time cause undue competition for the oak. This phase will continue to the thinning stage (height 12-15 m), by which time the conifers will have been removed.

On occasions, when the growth or stem form of the oak in parts of the stand is unsatisfactory and unlikely to attain the standard required, a different approach will be needed. In such situations the larch may be encouraged and retained as a mixture species for the rotation.

8.6.3.1.3 *Oak mixtures with other broadleaves*

For all 'monospecific' regular forests the objective for the main species determines the major line of action. In choosing a broadleaved mixture with oak some thought should be given to the respective growth rates and rotations of the species in the mixture, as well as to the function of these species. If the species is to compete with oak in the upper canopy, its growth rate should not be such that it will suppress the oak. On the other hand, if its function is to serve the development of the oak by remaining in the middle and lower storeys it must have shade bearing properties. Different rotation lengths of the species in mixture may cause problems in management later on when the trees are harvested, leading to openings in the stand and the risk of destabilisation. Oak, with its long rotation, will be the last species to be harvested; other species will usually be harvested earlier because of the risk of deterioration in quality. Therefore, the initial mixture should be so structured that, when harvested, its removal does not create large openings in the canopy, which could endanger the stability of the remaining oak or cause stem quality to deteriorate through the development of epicormic branches.

Broadleaved species to be considered in mixture with oak include hornbeam, lime, beech, sycamore and in exceptional cases ash and cherry. These can be grouped into (a) main forest species and (b) serving species. The principal function of the serving species is to perform a subsidiary role and aid in the development of the main species. Among the main forest species are sycamore, ash and cherry while hornbeam, beech and lime constitute the serving species.

(a) Mixtures of the main forest species, in groups or as single dominant trees with oak, are acceptable up to a level of 20% provided they are uniformly distributed throughout the stand.

Light demanding species, such as ash, cherry and sycamore often regenerate naturally in oak woodlands. On sites suited to these species, oak finds it difficult to compete in height growth in the early years. Furthermore, economic considerations, and the onset of degrade in quality, would indicate that ash and cherry should be harvested at 70 to 80 years of age, at a time when oak is only half way through its rotation.

Sycamore can remain for a longer period without deterioration in wood quality and be harvested with the oak.

(b) Hornbeam is a natural associate of the oak (especially pedunculate oak) in many continental countries but there are no examples of this mixture in Ireland. It is much more frost hardy than oak and grows less rapidly. Hornbeam is adapted to a wide range of soils and is more suited to the wetter, heavy clay soils than beech. For this reason it should be preferred to beech in mixture with pedunculate oak on such sites. The species should form an intimate mixture with the oak by planting a hornbeam every fourth tree in lines 2 m apart. Distance between plants in the lines should be 0.75 m. This gives a total of 6,600 plants/ha of which 1,600 will be hornbeam. It forms an effective understorey for the purpose of keeping the oak free of epicormic branches and the ground free of weed growth. Any tendency to usurp the place of the oak in the upper storey will, however, conflict with the main objective of high value oak production.

The role of oak/lime mixtures is similar to that of oak/hornbeam.

Beech forms an ideal middle and understorey for oak if its height growth is kept in check. Oak usually outgrows beech in the earlier stages but is inevitably overtaken by the beech in middle age. Beech is so resilient and aggressive that, on sites suited to its growth, it will overtake the oak at 70 to 80 years, when an understorey is most needed. For this reason oak/beech mixtures, at the establishment stage, are not recommended. The general practice is to introduce beech as an understorey at time of first thinning (see Section 2.3.10).

8.6.4   Vegetation management

Competition from grass and weeds is a major problem in all young crops. Vegetation control is therefore an essential operation and should be carried out until the plants are no longer threatened by competition from the vegetation (see Section 2.3.5).

8.7   FORMATIVE SHAPING

Although less sensitive than beech to injury by spring frost, the terminal bud of oak is often damaged or killed, particularly in low-lying locations. Damage to lammas shoots by early autumn frost and to emerging shoots by late spring frost contribute substantially to forking in oak. Formative shaping encourages the tree to revert to a single leader (see Section 2.3.6).

8.8   TENDING

Oak is a strong light demander so tending should begin when the crop reaches a top height of 6 - 7 m (see Section 2.3.7).

In naturally regenerated crops seedling densities can exceed 200,000 plants/ha but natural mortality will reduce this number to about one-half during the first few years. This will be reduced further at the sapling stage and differentiation into height classes will have occurred.

The first tending operation should reduce the upper storey (dominants and co-dominants) to about 3,600 trees/ha. This may be followed, if required, by a second intervention at a top height of 10 m, reducing the density to 1,900 to 2,100 trees/ha. At this stage naturally regenerated compatible species such as ash, wild cherry and sycamore are favoured.

With oak/conifer mixtures, tending should begin when the conifers start to interfere with the development of the oak but not later than a top height of 6 - 7 m when wolves and dominating conifers are removed. A second tending at a top height of 10 m will usually follow, to continue the removal of dominating conifers. If left unattended oak, as a light demanding species, will struggle to maintain its position in the upper canopy, often leading to etiolated stems with small crowns which are prone to the development of epicormic branching. This situation should be avoided.

In pure oak crops and those with an oak/hornbeam mixture, one tending operation at 6 - 8 m top height should suffice. This will reduce the stocking to about 2,800 - 3,000 trees/ha. If, due to poor stem form or absence of crown differentiation, a second intervention is deemed necessary it should be carried out at around 10 - 11 m top height and the stocking reduced to about 1,900 - 2,100 trees/ha. In mixed broadleaved stands hornbeam, which have entered the upper storey, should be cut back sufficiently to ensure that they do not present a threat to the oak dominants.

8.9 PRUNING

Pruning is an operation that is rarely cost effective, especially over long rotations. However, in oak/conifer mixtures the process of natural pruning may be so inadequate that artificial pruning may be required. Even in pure oak crops or oak/broadleaved mixtures situations may arise where some final crop candidates still have live branches at time of first thinning. In such circumstances it may be desirable to prune potential final crop stems on a limited scale. The branches on candidates for pruning should not have formed heartwood and should not exceed 3 cm in diameter at the stem. In addition the trees should possess good crowns, or have adequate shading from sub-dominants, otherwise they may respond by developing epicormic branches.

8.10 THINNING

More than any other broadleaved species, oak has a strong propensity to develop epicormic branches. In stands without a serving species a majority of stems will exhibit some tendency in this regard and thinning practice should avoid exacerbating this situation over the long term.

Epicormic branches arise from adventitious buds on the stem, which are activated by increased light within the stand, such as that resulting from heavy thinning. Conversely, small compressed crowns, which result from neglect of thinning, also induce epicormic branching as the trees struggle for survival. Provided light conditions are favourable, the epicormics continue to grow and will eventually form large branches if not shaded out by neighbours or an understorey. Even in the juvenile stage they give rise to clusters of small knots, or 'catspaws', in the wood, which makes it unsuitable for veneer or high-grade furniture.

The smaller the crowns, the greater the risk of epicormic branches developing. Even light thinnings may trigger the development of epicormic branching when the crowns are small or restricted. This presents the silviculturist with a dilemma. Light thinning will curb epicormic branching but will do little to develop the crowns and this in time may lead to the development of epicormics. Heavy crown thinning will allow the crowns to develop but may give rise to epicormic branching in the short term.

Traditionally, oak has been thinned cautiously; frequent and well-balanced interventions have been the norm. This has inevitably resulted in slow diameter growth and long rotations. Attempts to circumvent the difficulty have given rise to experimentation with 'free growth' in Britain and in Denmark, where some 50 - 60 final crop trees/ha have been isolated in youth by heavy thinning and the epicormics removed annually by pruning. The rapidly grown, large diameter and knot-free stems are said to be much sought after by timber merchants in Denmark. However, the procedure requires a commitment to annual pruning for a few generations.

In Germany old solitary, open-grown oak in meadows, although they carry large crowns, often contain a veneer length. This is due to the fact that cattle usually browse all branches and epicormics up to a height of 1.5 - 2.0 m.

Recent research on the treatment of oak in France and Germany favours a dynamic rather than a gradualist approach. It is predicated on the need for more rapid stem diameter growth and shorter rotations. Close spacing is maintained in youth to effect natural pruning and one or two early tendings ensure that wolves and poorly formed dominants are removed. When an adequate stem length (8 - 10 m) free of live branches is obtained, thinning of the upper canopy ensures good crown development and sufficient light for an understorey. The rationale is that early crown thinning allows one to optimise the potential of the juvenile growth phase for crown development, when the crop is most likely to respond. In turn, crown response to increased growing space helps to curb the stresses generated in the tree to produce epicormic branches. Furthermore, the increased incidence of light favours the growth of the understorey.

The differences in stocking densities between the French (upper storey only) dynamic schedules for sessile oak, site fertility classes I and II, and the gradualist approach implicit in the British model for yield class 8 oak, are shown in Figure 8.5. Although both sets of curves tend to converge at 17 - 18 m top height, the differences in youth, which reflect the different tending and thinning treatments, are fairly substantial.

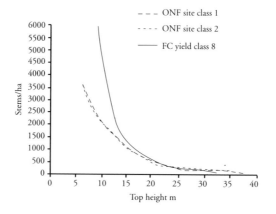

Figure 8.5: Relationships between top height and number of trees/ha in French (ONF) and British (FC) models.

Recommendations presented in section 8.1.2 are modelled on the French schedule for sessile oak classes I and II.

Stands of pedunculate oak, or those mainly composed of that species, may need a different schedule. Pedunculate oak grows more rapidly and has a more spreading crown than sessile. Its recommended thinning schedules should reflect these differences with lower stocking density for a given top height.

According to the schedule presented in section 8.1.2, thinning begins when the top height is about 14 m. This reduces the stocking density to about 1,200 trees/ha. In normal stands, the potential final crop trees, identified in tending, should have about 8-10 m of stem length free of live branches (see Section 2.3.9).

The first thinning is followed by the selection of final crop trees. In selecting final crop trees, vitality of the tree and quality of stem takes precedence over uniformity of spacing (in that order).

In pure oak stands and in oak/conifer mixtures (from which most, if not all, conifers will have been removed), preparations should be made for the establishment of an understorey (see Section 2.3.10).

Subsequent thinnings should take place at 1.5 - 2 m increments in top height. Interventions take the form of selective crown thinnings of medium intensity to favour the development of the final crop tree candidates by removing competitors. These competitors will be trees that threaten to dominate the selected final crop trees or to compress their crowns. Thinning should continue to promote the development of the understorey, gradually and cautiously.

If tending or thinning has been delayed, the provision of growing space for the selected final crop trees should be approached cautiously, particularly if the crowns are small. Unlike beech, oak can only enlarge its crown upwards and needs more time for crown development. Therefore, thinnings should be lighter and more frequent. Thinning must also have regard to developing the understorey and must be of sufficient intensity to encourage its development. However, one is warned not to thin too heavily. Thinning intervention must tread a fine line between the danger from epicormic branching (from too heavy thinning) on the one hand, and the light requirements of the understorey (the fear of damage to the understorey by shading) on the other.

For oak, more than for any other species, continuous and well-balanced intervention treatments determine the amount of high value timber generated in the stand.

Old oak stands respond poorly to increased growing space. Pedunculate oak from age 100, and sessile from age 120, may respond to thinning by developing epicormic branches. From then on, thinning intervention in the form of occasional felling is only required to remove diseased and damaged stems and achieve the necessary stem reduction for the development of the final crop, the encouragement of the middle and lower storeys and the removal of competing beech.

Suggested average thinning cycles are provided in Table 8.4

Table 8.4: Thinning cycles for oak

Pedunculate oak		Sessile oak	
Age interval years	Thinning cycle years	Age interval years	Thinning cycle years
30 - 45	8	40 - 100	8
45 - 75	10	100 - 170	10
75 - 120	16		

8.11   UNDERPLANTING

Normally, pure oak stands have a low standing volume/ha at maturity (250-300 m^3/ha) combined with a strong tendency to develop epicormic branches during the rotation, particularly if crowns are restricted or thinning is heavy. Provision of an understorey assists in natural pruning with consequent improvement in wood quality. Furthermore, an understorey will increase the stand volume production and give greater flexibility in management. The species most suitable for the purpose are hornbeam and beech (see Section 2.3.10).

Planting beech in mixture with oak at time of establishment is not recommended. Although oak will outgrow beech in the early stages of development the beech will assume dominance midway through the rotation, at a time when an understorey is needed. The preferred procedure is to underplant the oak with beech (or hornbeam) after the first thinning.

Glossary

Auricle   An appendage, which may resemble the ear of an animal, occurring at the base of a leaf-blade.

BP   Before present - a measure of time in years from the present to the occurrence of a past event.

Basal area   The cross-sectional area of a tree measured at 1.3 m (breast height) from the ground surface.

Climax species   The species in the final stage of plant succession which reaches a state of equilibrium with the environment.

Co-dominant trees   Trees in the upper canopy (which they help to complete) but which are below the crown level of the dominants.

Coppice system   Crops, in part at least, originating from stool shoots (coppice) or by other vegetative means.

Coppice with standards   Crops consisting partly of vegetative shoots and partly of trees generally of seedling origin.

Crown thinning   The removal of dominant trees to provide growing space for the potential final crop trees. It involves the removal of diseased, dead and leaning trees, defective dominants, some of the well-formed dominants where they are grouped, and part of the co-dominants. The sub-dominant and suppressed trees are retained but the worst trees in these classes may be cut out to favour the best. This is the standard thinning for broadleaves.

Dbh   Diameter breast height - diameter of the stem measured at 1.3 m above ground level. (Mean stand diameter is the quadratic mean, the diameter corresponding to the mean basal area tree (see above).)

Dioecious   Possessing male and female flowers on separate unisexual individual plants.

Dominant trees   These are the tallest and the most vigorous trees in the crop, and usually have a large proportion of their crowns free.

Earlywood   Thin-walled cells with large spaces (lumina) within the cell walls, formed in the annual ring at the commencement of growth in spring.

Epicormic branches	Small branchlets originating from adventitious buds on the stem. They are found on all broadleaved species but are most serious on oak.
Fastigiate branching	Branching sloping towards the vertical, making an acute angle with the stem and with generally parallel branches.
Genotype	The genetic constitution of an organism, as opposed to its physical appearance (phenotype).
Group system	A shelterwood system of successive regeneration fellings in which the canopy is opened by removing trees in scattered groups.
Latewood	Thick walled cells (with small lumina) formed in the annual growth ring during the summer and early autumn period.
Mast year	A year in which seed is produced in exceptionally large quantities. Refers mainly to beech and oaks which produce 'mast years' at intervals of 5 - 15 years in Ireland. The quantity of seed produced is conditioned by the amount of sunshine the previous summer.
Monoecious	A plant which bears separate male and female flowers on the same plant.
Monopodial	A plant with a single axis or stem and extension growth from the apex.
Natural regeneration	The regeneration of a crop through seeds from mother trees on the ground or in the vicinity.
Pelosol	Fine textured clay soil.
pH	A value on a scale 0 - 14 that gives a measure of the acidity or alkalinity of a soil. A neutral soil has a pH of 7. Acidic soils have pH values of less than 7 and alkaline soils have values greater than 7. The lower the pH the more acidic is the soil; the higher the pH the more alkaline.
Phenotype	The observed characteristics of a tree, produced by the genotype in conjunction with the environment.
Pinnate	Of leaves, compound, with leaflets displayed on either side of a central stalk.
Pioneer species	Species that colonise a physical environment sequentially until a final equilibrium state, the climax, is achieved.
Provenance	A geographical area of occurrence of a particular species, for example 'Spessart oak' from south-central Germany.

Pruning	The removal of branches from a tree stem by artificial or natural means.
Riverine	Located in the vicinity of a river (usually in the flood-plain).
Rotation	The number of years required to establish and grow a crop to a specified condition of maturity, at which stage the crop is felled (clear felling) or regenerated under the shelter of the existing crop (shelterwood), which is then gradually removed.
Serving species	A species whose function is to remain in the middle and lower storeys and perform a shading role which assists in natural pruning and suppresses ground vegetation. The species must have shade bearing characteristics.
Shelterwood system	A silvicultural system of successive regeneration fellings in which the young crop is established under the partial shade, overhead or lateral, of the old crop.
Silviculture	The science of establishing, growing and managing forest crops.
Silvicultural system	The process by which the forest crops are tended, thinned, removed and replaced by new crops, resulting in stands of distinctive form.
Sprouting	Beginning to grow; giving off shoots or buds.
Sub-dominant trees	These trees are not in the upper canopy but their leaders still have free access to the light.
Sucker shoots	An underground shoot arising adventitiously from the roots or lower stem of a tree and emerging from the soil to form a new plant, initially nourished by its parent.
Suppressed trees	These are trees whose leaders have no direct access to light and stand beneath the crowns of adjacent trees.
Sympodial	A type of branching in which an apparent main axis is made up of many lateral branches, each arising from the one before.
Taproot	The main descending central root.
Tending	The removal of wolves and trees of defective stem form which would adversely affect the growth and quality of the crop. This is usually done at a top height of 5 - 8 m.
Thinning	The removal of a proportion of trees from an immature crop in order to improve the growth and form of the remainder.

Thinning cycle	The interval in years between successive thinnings.
Uniform system	A shelterwood system in which successive regeneration fellings are uniformly distributed over the whole compartment, resulting in a more or less even-aged crops.
Wildings	Self-sown plants.
Wolves	Trees in the upper canopy (dominants/co-dominants) with defective stems and large, rough lateral branches.
Yield class	The potential or actual yield. In Britain and Ireland it is calculated as the total volume production (m^3/ha) divided by age at time of culmination of mean annual increment. German yield class is defined in a different manner: it is the potential mean annual volume increment (m^3/ha) at 100 years of age. Thus, yield class 9 is equivalent to a cumulative volume production of 900 m^3/ha at 100 years of age.

Bibliography

1   INTRODUCTION

Baillie, M.G.L. and D. M. Brown. 1995. Some deductions on ancient Irish trees from
            dendrochronology. In Wood, Trees and Forests in Ireland; Eds. Jon R.
            Pilcher and Sean Mac an tSaoir. Royal Irish Academy, Dublin.

Cubbage, F.W. and W.C. Siegel. 1985. The Law Regulating Private Forest Practices.
            Journal of Forestry, Vol. 83, No. 9.

Durand, J.F. 1969. The Evolution of State Forestry in Ireland. Unpublished PhD thesis,
            N.U.I. (UCD).

Fitzpatrick, H. M. 1966. The Forests of Ireland. Society of Irish Foresters.

Hall, V. A. 1995. Woodland depletion in Ireland over the last millennium. In Wood,
            Trees and Forests in Ireland; Eds. Jon R. Pilcher and Sean Mac an tSaoir.
            Royal Irish Academy, Dublin.

Hayes, S. 1822. A Practical Treatise on Planting; and The Management of Woods and
            Coppices; Third Edition. Samuel Jones, 8 Trinity Street, Dublin.

Jones, M. 1986. Coppice Wood Management in the Eighteenth Century: an Example
            from County Wicklow. Irish Forestry, Vol. 43, No. 1.

Mc Cracken, E. 1971. The Irish Woods since Tudor Times. David and Charles,
            Newton Abbot.

Mitchell, F. 1976. The Irish Landscape. Collins, London.

Mitchell, F. J. G. 1995. The dynamics of Irish post-glacial forests. In Wood, Trees and
            Forests in Ireland; Eds. Jon R. Pilcher and Sean Mac an tSaoir. Royal Irish
            Academy, Dublin.

Neeson, E. 1991. A History of Irish Forestry. The Lilliput Press Ltd. Dublin.

OCarroll, N. 1995. Forestry in the Republic of Ireland - an industry in transition. In
            Wood, Trees and Forests in Ireland; Eds. Jon R. Pilcher and Sean Mac an
            tSaoir. Royal Irish Academy, Dublin.

OCarroll, N. 1997. Irish Forestry - an investment for prosperity. Irish Forestry,
            Vol. 54, No. 1.

Racham, O. 1995. Looking for ancient woodland in Ireland. In Wood, Trees and Forests
            in Ireland; Eds. Jon R. Pilcher and Sean Mac an tSaoir. Royal Irish
            Academy, Dublin.

2   **SILVICULTURAL STRATEGY AND PROCEDURES**

Anon. 1996. Growing for the Future; A Strategic Plan for the Development of the Forestry Sector in Ireland. The Stationery Office, Dublin

Culleton, N., W. E. Murphy and R. R. Hicks, Jr. 1995. Competition Control for Establishment of Ash (*Fraxinus excelsior* L.) on Lowland Soil in Ireland. Irish Forestry, Vol. 52, Nos. 1 and 2.

3   **SOILS**

Evans, J. 1984. Silviculture of Broadleaved Woodland. Forestry Commission Bulletin 62. HMSO, London.

Harris, E. 1987. The case for sycamore. Quarterly Journal of Forestry, Vol. LXXXI, No. 1.

Hodge, S. J. 1995. Creating and Managing Woodlands Around Towns. Forestry Commission. Handbook 11. HMSO, London.

4   **ASH**

Anon. No year given. The Management of Semi-Natural Woodlands; Upland Mixed Ashwoods. Forestry Practice Guide 4. Forestry Practice Division, The Forest Authority, Edinburgh.

Culleton, N., W. E. Murphy and A. McLoughlin. 1996. The use of fertilisers in the establishment phase of common ash (*Fraxinus excelsior* L.). Irish Forestry, Vol. 53, Nos. 1 and 2.

Fitzsimons, B. and W. B. Luddy. 1986. Growing Ash for Hurleys. Irish Forestry, Vol. 43, No. 1.

Pilard-Landeau, B. *et* N. Le Goff. 1996. *Sylviculture du Frêne. Office National des Forêts.* Bulletin Technique No. 31.

Volquardts, G. 1958: *Ertragstafel Esche.* In: Yield Tables of Forest Service Baden Württemberg, 1993.

Wimmenauer, K. 1919: *Wachstum und Ertrag der Esche.* Allg. Forst- u. J. Ztg. 95: 2 - 17.

5   **SYCAMORE**

Binggeli, P. and B. S. Rushton. 1997. The Potential of Sycamore and Ash in Irish and British Forestry - a Review. University of Ulster, Northern Ireland. (Unpublished Report to COFORD).

Hassenkamp. W. 1959. Review of contributions by Kjölby, Sabroe and Moltesen on *Aer (Acer pseudoplatanus)*, in *Dansk Skovforening.* 1958. Forstarchiv. 138 - 140.

Kjölby, V. 1958. History, yield and harvesting of sycamore. In Hassenkamp, 1959.

Nagel, J. 1986. *Wachstumsmodell für Bergahorn in Schleswig-Holstein.* Allg. Forst- u. J. Ztg. 157: 31-36.

Stern, R. C. 1982. The use of sycamore in British forestry. In Broadleaves in Britain; Eds.   D. C. Malcolm, J. Evans and P.N. Edwards. Camera-ready copy by Publication Preparation Service. Produced by Edinburgh University Press. Printed in Great Britain by Redwood Burn Ltd., Trowbridge, G.B.

Stevenson, G. F. 1985. The silviculture of ash and sycamore. In National Hardwood Programme, Commonwealth Forestry Institute, Oxford.

6   WILD CHERRY

Anon. 1993. *Empfehlungen zum Anbau der Wildkirsche.* (Unpublished script for the Forest Service.) Düsseldorf: *Ministerium für Umwelt, Raumordnung und Landwirtschaft des Landes Nordrhein-Westfalen* (ed. 1992).

Harrington, R. 1997. How much do you know about cherry? Irish Timber & Forestry. Sept./Oct. issue.

Knaggs, G. 1997. Cherry - The timber. Irish Timber & Forestry. Sept./Oct. issue.

Pryor, S. N. 1988. The silviculture and yield of wild cherry. Forestry Commission Bulletin 75. HMSO. London.

Spiecker, M. 1994. *Wachstum und Erziehung wertvoller Waldkirchen. Mitteilungen der Forstlichen Versuchs- und Forschungsanstalt Baden-Württemberg. Heft* 181.

Zeitlinger, H. J. 1990. *Die Vogelkirche.* Österr. Forstzeitung. 31-34.

7   BEECH

Duplat, P. *et* B. Roman-Amat, *avec la collaboration de* F. Chollet, C. Demolis, E. Kiefer. 1996. *Sylviculture du Hêtre. Office National des Forêts.* Bulletin Technique No. 31.

Schober, R. 1967: *Ertragstafel Buche.* (Forest Service Baden-Württemberg.)

Schober, R. 1971: *Die Rotbuche.* In Nagel, J. 1986.

8   OAK

Anon. No year given. The Management of Semi-Natural Woodlands; Upland Oakwoods. Forestry Practice Guide 5. Forestry Practice Division, The Forest Authority, Edinburgh

Duplat, P. *avec la participation de* P. Champagne, F. Chollet, C. Ginisty, P. Jarret, M. Nouveau, F. Reteau, E. Sevrin. 1996. *Sylviculture du Chêne pédonculé. Office National des Forêts.* Bulletin Technique No. 31.

Jarret, P. *avec la participation de* P. Duplat, H. Hoyau, E. Kiefer. 1996. *Sylviculture du Chêne sessile. Office National des Forêts.* Bulletin Technique No. 31.

Jobling, J. and M. L. Pearce. 1987. Free Growth of Oak. Forest Record No. 113, Forestry Commission. London. HMSO.

Jüttner, O. 1955. *Ertragstafel Eiche.* In *Ministerium für Ländlichen Raum, Ernährung und Forsten.* Baden-Württemberg (ed. 1993). *Hilfstafeln für die Forsteinrichtung.* Stuttgart. pp188.

Kerr, G. 1996. The effect of heavy or 'free growth' thinning on oak (*Quercus petraea* and *Q. robur*). Forestry, Vol. 69, No. 4.

Oswald, H. 1981. *Résultats principaux des places d'expérience de Chêne du Centre national de Recherches forestières. Sylvicultures en futaies feuillues.* Revue Forestière Française. Vol. 33, *numero special,* 1981.

Oswald, H. 1982. Sylviculture of oak and beech high forests in France. In Broadleaves in Britain; Eds. D. C. Malcolm, J. Evans and P.N. Edwards. Camera-ready copy by Publication Preparation Service. Produced by Edinburgh University Press. Printed in Great Britain by Redwood Burn Ltd., Trowbridge, G.B.

Savill, P. S. and R. A. Mather. 1990. A Possible Indicator of Shake in Oak: Relationship between Flushing Date and Vessel Sizes. Forestry, Vol. 63, No. 4.

9.   **GENERAL**

Anon. No year given. The Management of Semi-Natural Woodlands; Lowland Acid Beech & Oak Woods. Forestry Practice Guide1. Forestry Practice Division, The Forest Authority, Edinburgh.

Anon. No year given. The Management of Semi-Natural Woodlands. Lowland Beech-Ash Woods. Forestry Practice Guide 2. Forestry Practice Division, The Forest Authority, Edinburgh.

Anon. No year given. The Management of Semi-Natural Woodlands; Lowland Mixed Broadleaved Woods. Forestry Practice Guide 3. Forestry Practice Division, The Forest Authority. Edinburgh.

Anon. 1984. British Standard Nursery Stock, Specification for Forest Trees (BS 3936: Part 4: 1984).

Anon. 1992. *Waldbaurichtlinien für die Wälder von Rheinland-Pfalz. 2. Teil. Landesforstverwaltung Rheinland-Pfalz,* Mainz.

Anon. 1993. Coillte, Research and Development, 1993. Broadleaves: Guidelines for their successful establishment.

Anon. 1993. *Mitteleuropäische Waldbaumarten: Artbeschreibung und Ökologie unter besonderer Berücksichtigung der Schweiz,* (unpublished). Zürich: *Professur für Waldbau und Professur für Forstschutz & Dendrologie der ETH.*

Anon, 1994. Afforestation Guidelines for the Preparation of a Report at Pre-Planting Stage. (Internal Document, Forest Service, Dublin).

Bolton, Lord. 1956. Profitable Forestry. Faber and Faber Limited, London.

Brown, J. and J. Nisbet. 1894. The Forester, Vol. I; Sixth Edition. William Blackwood and Sons. Edinburgh.

Bulfin, M and T. Radford. 1997. A general guide to early formative shaping of broadleaves. Teagasc, Kinsealy Research Centre.

Burschel P. and J. Huss. 1997. *Grundriß des Waldbaus.* 2nd revised and extended edition. Berlin: Parey Buchverlag. pp 487.

Denne, M. P. and R.S. Dodd. 1982. Some dissatisfied thoughts about the wood quality of British Broadleaves. In Broadleaves in Britain; Eds. D. C. Malcolm, J. Evans and P. N. Edwards. Camera-ready copy by Publication Preparation Service. Produced by Edinburgh University Press. Printed in Great Britain by Redwood Burn Ltd., Trowbridge, G.B.

Duncan, H.W. 1996. A case for planting broadleaves at wide spacing. Scottish Forestry. Vol. 50. No. 4.

Edlin, H. L. 1969. What Wood is That? Stobart & Sons Ltd. London.

Edlin, H.L. 1985. Broadleaves. Forestry Commission Booklet No. 20. HMSO. London.

Evans, J. 1984. Silviculture of Broadleaved Woodland. Forestry Commission Bulletin 62. H.M.S.O. London.

Garfitt, J. E. 1995. Natural management of woods: continuous cover forestry. Research Studies Press Ltd. Taunton, Somerset, England. John Wiley & Sons Inc.

Hamilton, G. J. and J. M. Christie. 1971. Forest Management Tables (Metric). Forestry Commission Booklet No. 34. HMSO, London.

Hummel, F. C., G.M.L. Locke, J. N. R. Jeffers and J. M. Christie. 1959. Code of Sample Plot Procedure. Forestry Commission Bulletin No. 31. H.M.S.O. London.

Huss, J. 1995. Broadleaves - An alternative to conifers in Ireland. Irish Forestry, Vol. 52 Nos. 1 & 2.

Johnston, D. R., A. J. Grayson and R.T. Bradley. 1967. Forest Planning. Faber and Faber Ltd. London.

Jørgensen, A. 1995. A review of afforestation and broadleaves in Irish Forestry. Internal report to Coillte (unpublished).

Kerr, G. and J. Evans. 1993. Growing Broadleaves for Timber. Forestry Commission Handbook 9. H.M.S.O. London.

Lincoln, W. A. 1986. World Woods in Colour. Stobart & Sons Ltd. London.

Low, A. J. 1986. Use of Broadleaved Species in Upland Forests. Leaflet No. 88, Forestry Commission, London. H.M.S.O.

Matthews, J. D. 1989. Silvicultural Systems. Clarendon Press, Oxford.

Nelson E. C. and W. F. Walsh. 1993. Trees of Ireland, Native and Naturalized. The Lilliput Press, Dublin.

Peterken, G. F. 1994. Woodland Conservation and Management. Second Edition. Chapman & Hall, London.

Peterken, G. F. 1996. Natural Woodland; Ecology and Conservation in Northern Temperate Regions. Cambridge University Press.

Pfeifer, A., K. Hutchinson, J. Neilan and F. Shekleton. 1990. Report of Working Party on Broadleaves. Coillte internal document.

Rowe, J. J. 1980. Grey squirrel control. Forestry Commission. HMSO. London.

Savill, P. S. 1992. The silviculture of trees used in British forestry. C. A. B. International, Wallingford, Oxon. U. K.

Schlich, W. 1889. A Manual of Forestry, Vol. I. Bradbury, Agnew & Co. London.

Schlich, W. 1891. A Manual of Forestry, Vol. II. Bradbury, Agnew & Co. London.

Schweingruber, F. H. 1990. Microscopic Wood Anatomy. Swiss Federal Institute for Forest, Snow and Landscape Research.

Ward, D. 1996. Guidelines for the use of herbicides in forestry. Forest Service, Dublin.

Appendix

FOREST	PROPERTY	COMPARTMENT	SUB - COMP	SPECIES
Adare	Curragh Chase	41007M	2	Ash
Arigna	Knockrannt	67164K	2	Ash
Athenry	Kilcornan	51029E	14	Ash
Athenry	Kilcornan	51030U	4	Ash
Ballygar	Dressmakers Wood	55382T	8	Ash
Ballygar	Dressmakers Wood	55383O	2	Ash
Ballynoe	Rincrew	28055A	2	Ash
Banteer	Ballygiblin	35252Q	1	Ash
Banteer	Boolymore	35309E	6	Ash
Benbulben	Lissadell	61155N	1	Ash
Benbulben	Lissadell	61155N	9	Ash
Boyle	Errironagh	68063O	6	Ash
Boyle	Errironagh	68067R	4	Ash
Broadford	Dromoland	41470A	4	Ash
Broadford	Dromoland	41471S	1	Ash
Bunclody	Carriglead	17005B	4	Ash
Callan	Desart	21008C	8	Ash
Callan	Knockadrina	21382J	7	Ash
Cappoquin	Salterbridge	27184L	11	Ash
Castlecomer	Jenkinstown	21164C	4	Ash
Clonmel	Curtiswood	23753B	7	Ash
Cong	Ballykine	51755D	12	Ash
Cong	Ballykine	51757Q	8	Ash
Coolgreaney	Barnadown	17733N	3	Ash
Coolgreaney	Kerrs	17740W	5	Ash
Cuilcagh	Derrycarne	67959E	10	Ash
Curraghmore	Knocknacrhy	23438J	4	Ash
Ennis	Dangan	42453M	2	Ash
Glencree	Massey Estate	11783T	15	Ash
Graiguenamanagh	Fiddaun	21889I	3	Ash
Killavullen	Dromdeer	35193R	3	Ash
Lough owel	Newcastle	73129J	3	Ash
Midleton	Deerpark	31786V	2	Ash
Portumna	Demesne	55852C	2	Ash
Portumna	Demesne	55864J	9	Ash
Portumna	Demesne	55865E	2	Ash
Rathdangan	Mullaghreelan	15040S	1	Ash
Shillelagh	Balisland	16136C	4	Ash
Shillelagh	Killalongford	16248C	9	Ash
Adare	Curragh Chase	41004E	1	Beech
Allen	Donadea	11252U	3	Beech
Athenry	Kilcornan	51029E	6	Beech
Athenry	Kilcornan	51030U	1	Beech
Athenry	Kilcornan	51030U	2	Beech
Athenry	Kilcornan	51030U	3	Beech
Athenry	Kilcornan	51030U	5	Beech
Athenry	Kilcornan	51031P	5	Beech
Athenry	Kilcornan	51032K	3	Beech
Athenry	Ballindereen	51092U	1	Beech
Aughrim	Mangans	16217C	1	Beech
Aughrim	Mangans	16217C	2	Beech
Avoca	Ballyarthur	81403O	16	Beech
Avonmore	Ballyteige	13977K	2	Beech
Ballynoe	Rincrew	28055A	6	Beech
Benbulben	Hazelwood	61807H	2	Beech
Benbulben	Hazelwood	61808C	2	Beech
Benbulben	Hazelwood	61808C	1	Beech
Blessington	Kippure	11048K	5	Beech
Blessington	Ballydonnel	11049F	2	Beech
Blessington	Glenaraneen	12052D	5	Beech
Broadford	Dromoland	41469H	1	Beech
Bunclody	Bahana	17007O	1	Beech
Callan	Desart	21008C	7	Beech

P/YEAR	STOCKING trees/ha	TOP HEIGHT m	DBH cm	ELEVATION m	SOILTYPE
1945	800	14	17	15	Grey brown podzolic
1951	300	20	28	55	Grey brown podzolic
1937	500	16	20	15	Shallow brown earth/Rendzina
1953	300	16	23	20	Shallow brown earth/Rendzina
1977	700	12	11	60	Grey brown podzolic
1954	1000	22	27	60	Grey brown podzolic
1965	150	15	25	75	Brown earth
1949	1200	18	20	90	Brown earth
1972	2500	12	13	150	Brown earth
1910	200	20	25	10	Grey brown podzolic
1910	300	15	28	15	Grey brown podzolic
1962	1200	12	8	60	Grey brown podzolic
1930	300	15	20	50	Grey brown podzolic
1963	500	16	18	15	Brown earth
1960	800	10	12	60	Brown earth
1940	300	16	20	30	Brown earth
1943	100	22	19	80	Brown earth
1949	400	20	15	120	Brown earth
1968	900	14	13	70	Brown earth
1944	500	15	18	90	Brown earth
1972	5000	17	9	130	Acid brown earth
1986	150	2	-	35	Brown earth
1985	200	3	-	35	Rendzina
1939	600	16	15	26	Gley
1958	800	14	15	40	Gley
1940	100	13	18	60	Gley
1939	800	15	16	70	Brown earth
1951	1000	13	15	30	Shallow brown earth/Rendzina
1938	100	18	30	230	Brown earth
1975	2000	11	13	70	Gley
1956	800	15	12	75	Gley
1946	200	20	28	55	Brown earth
1941	100	22	30	60	Brown podzolic
1970	1500	11	10	40	Grey brown podzolic
1940	400	25	25	45	Grey brown podzolic
1940	100	25	45	40	Grey brown podzolic
1950	200	18	20	90	Grey brown podzolic
1954	900	14	11	60	Brown podzolic
1956	1000	10	12	180	Brown podzolic
1877	100	20	60	30	Brown earth
1950	300	23	35	100	Grey brown podzolic
1937	600	16	30	25	Grey brown podzolic
1954	400	16	25	20	Grey brown podzolic
1920	200	25	50	20	Grey brown podzolic
1953	300	16	25	15	Grey brown podzolic
1953	400	20	25	25	Grey brown podzolic
1938	500	16	32	25	Grey brown podzolic
1945	500	16	35	25	Grey brown podzolic
1880	200	18	40	20	Grey brown podzolic
1956	900	14	18	230	Brown podzolic
1956	1000	12	16	230	Podzol
1944	650	25	25	90	Brown earth
1914	300	25	30	220	Brown earth
1780	250	22	50	90	Brown earth
1940	500	20	25	30	Brown earth
1941	600	20	22	15	Grey brown podzolic
1941	500	16	22	30	Grey brown podzolic
1850	100	23	70	280	Grey brown podzolic
1880	100	25	65	300	Grey brown podzolic
1940	500	22	25	280	Podzol
1960	900	14	20	60	Grey brown podzolic
1942	500	19	28	25	Brown podzolic
1943	200	23	24	80	Brown earth

FOREST	PROPERTY	COMPARTMENT	SUB - COMP	SPECIES
Callan	Castlemorres	21352E	4	Beech
Callan	Grangecrag	44450L	1	Beech
Callan	Kyle	44471R	2	Beech
Cappoquin	Glenshelane	27197N	3	Beech
Cappoquin	Knocknasheega	27731O	10	Beech
Castlecomer	Dunmore	21122N	5	Beech
Castlecomer	Haywood	21139S	1	Beech
Castlecomer	Jenkinstown	21163H	7	Beech
Castlecomer	Jenkinstown	21164C	6	Beech
Castlecomer	Jenkinstown	21167K	2	Beech
Cong	Ballykine	51751A	3	Beech
Cong	Ballykine	51753N	1	Beech
Cong	Ballykine	51754I	2	Beech
Cong	Ballykine	51754I	3	Beech
Cong	Ballykine	51757Q	3	Beech
Cong	Ballykine	51757Q	11	Beech
Cong	Ballykine	51758L	8	Beech
Cong	Ballykine	51759G	4	Beech
Cong	Ballykine	51759G	7	Beech
Curraghmore	Brownstown	23124K	4	Beech
Dundalk	Black island	72135I	4	Beech
Emo	Emo park	77508M	1	Beech
Emo	Kilbride	77518G	8	Beech
Emo	Carrick Wood	77527F	1	Beech
Emo	Rathleash	77529S	1	Beech
Ennis	Moyriesk	42464B	1	Beech
Forth	Lacken	17989I	2	Beech
Galtee	Boolaghkennedy	25945N	3	Beech
Glencree	Deerpark	11677B	1	Beech
Graiguenamanagh	Woodstock	21861O	3	Beech
Kenmare	Dromore	45613V	5	Beech
Killane	Kilbora	17485R	2	Beech
Killavullen	Ballyduff	31551J	2	Beech
Kilsheelan	Glen	23584P	1	Beech
Kilsheelan	Glen	23606A	5	Beech
Midleton	Rostellan	31803I	3	Beech
Monaghan	Benwilt	71592N	2	Beech
Monaghan	Rossmore	72105D	1	Beech
Monasterevan	Mooreabbey	74815B	1	Beech
Mullinavat	Garryduff	21612H	10	Beech
Portlaoise	Sheffield	77987K	6	Beech
Portlaoise	Dysart	77993B	3	Beech
Portlaoise	Oughaval	78056T	1	Beech
Portlaoise	Oughaval	78057O	1	Beech
Rathdangan	Dollardstown	15034E	7	Beech
Rathdangan	Dollardstown	15036R	13	Beech
Silvermines	Knockanacre	43938C	2	Beech
Swanlinbar	Portlongfield	71821Q	4	Beech
Virginia	Demesne	71008D	2	Beech
Virginia	Headfort	71022V	7	Beech
Virginia	Mullaghmeen	71307K	1	Beech
Virginia	Mullaghmeen	71308F	13	Beech
Virginia	Mullaghmeen	71313B	1	Beech
Virginia	Mullaghmeen	71314T	2	Beech
Virginia	Halfcarton	71316J	5	Beech
Virginia	Bigwood	71337P	1	Beech
Allen	Rahin	11407L	1	Oak
Avonmore	Ballyganon Wood	13901N	1	Oak
Avonmore	Killeagh	81392S	1	Oak
Avonmore	Stafford's Avenue	81395D	1	Oak
Ballygar	Aghrane	55313K	4	Oak

P/YEAR	STOCKING trees/ha	TOP HEIGHT m	DBH cm	ELEVATION m	SOILTYPE
1937	500	18	26	200	Podzol
1910	175	22	35	210	Brown earth
1942	250	22	26	200	Shallow brown earth
1910	300	23	42	60	Grey brown podzolic
1960	3000	15	11	220	Brown earth
1950	500	20	26	90	Grey brown podzolic
1942	500	18	24	140	Brown earth
1941	120	18	30	80	Brown earth
1941	150	20	32	90	Brown earth
1943	150	20	40	80	Brown earth
1943	800	20	23	40	Shallow brown earth/Rendzina
1941	600	20	28	35	Shallow brown earth/Rendzina
1940	600	22	28	35	Shallow brown earth/Rendzina
1941	600	18	25	35	Shallow brown earth/Rendzina
1943	400	22	26	35	Shallow brown earth/rendzina
1941	150	16	35	50	Shallow brown earth/Rendzina
1940	400	20	25	35	Shallow brown earth/Rendzina
1941	600	20	32	35	Shallow brown earth/Rendzina
1941	500	20	26	35	Shallow brown earth/Rendzina
1955	600	16	21	130	Brown earth
1952	250	14	26	100	Acid brown earth
1937	220	25	33	100	Brown earth
1939	250	22	30	75	Brown earth
1934	400	22	25	90	Brown earth
1945	175	20	35	90	Brown earth
1963	800	14	22	20	Brown earth
1942	1200	15	21	85	Brown earth
1975	120	7	12	180	Podzol
1956	600	15	19	120	Grey brown podzolic
1937	400	14	18	25	Brown podzolic
1780	50	22	100	60	Podzol
1941	1000	18	27	90	Brown podzolic
1950	700	16	25	90	Brown podzolic
1938	200	16	22	130	Brown earth
1956	300	17	28	30	Brown podzolic
1880	90	25	100	5	Brown earth
1939	400	17	32	95	Brown earth
1953	400	16	28	100	Acid brown earth
1954	1000	20	25	100	Grey brown podzolic
1955	900	15	25	250	Acid brown earth
1939	200	17	22	130	Brown earth
1943	200	20	27	180	Brown earth
1937	200	18	25	180	Grey brown podzolic
1938	220	24	28	140	Grey brown podzolic
1890	150	27	45	75	Brown earth
1935	2000	13	13	75	Shallow brown earth
1954	900	13	18	110	Brown earth
1900	400	25	35	55	Gley
1931	350	18	31	150	Acid brown earth
1938	600	18	27	95	Acid brown earth
1937	450	18	25	190	Grey brown podzolic
1937	350	16	23	200	Grey brown podzolic
1936	300	22	26	90	Grey brown podzolic
1936	400	23	25	90	Grey brown podzolic
1944	350	20	25	95	Brown earth
1954	800	13	17	120	Brown earth
1938	300	22	25	100	Grey brown podzolic
1870	200	20	56	140	Podzol
1860	220	23	32	60	Brown earth
1850	60	25	65	60	Gley/Brown podzolic
1942	300	18	20	55	Grey brown podzolic

FOREST	PROPERTY	COMPARTMENT	SUB - COMP	SPECIES
Bantry	Demesne	33602L	5	Oak
Bantry	Demesne	33603G	1	Oak
Benbulben	Glencar	61833J	9	Oak
Boyle	Errironagh	68066W	7	Oak
Broadford	Doon	41306T	2	Oak
Broadford	Voilet Hill	41308J	3	Oak
Bunclody	Bahana	17008J	3	Oak
Callan	Monarche	21024K	1	Oak
Callan	Kilcooly	44401N	3	Oak
Callan	Grangecrag	44443C	2	Oak
Cappoquin	Glentaun	27182V	1	Oak
Cappoquin	Glenribbeen	27183Q	1	Oak
Castlecomer	Dunmore	21121S	1	Oak
Coolgreaney	Camolin	17455M	16	Oak
Coolgreaney	Ballyfad	81260H	1	Oak
Croagh Patrick	Brackloon	53277A	5	Oak
Croagh Patrick	Old Head	53584L	1	Oak
Cuilcagh	Lough Rynn	67991U	1	Oak
Curraghmore	Glenhouse	23436T	6	Oak
Dungarvan	Dromana	27158J	5	Oak
Fermoy	Castlecooke	35950A	1	Oak
Galtee	Glengara Wood	25903B	15	Oak
Glendalough	Laragh	13331O	1	Oak
Glendalough	Ballard	13842O	1	Oak
Glenealy	Ballymanus	13405F	1	Oak
Glenealy	Ballymanus	13405F	2	Oak
Glenealy	Ballymanus	13410B	1	Oak
Glenealy	Ballydowling	13993S	1	Oak
Kenmare	Dromore	45610N	5	Oak
Killavullen	Dreenagh Wood	35214H	1	Oak
Killavullen	Monaduhana	35215C	3	Oak
Killavullen	Monaduhana	35215C	9	Oak
Killavullen	Dromdeer	35216U	1	Oak
Lough Eske	Friary	66318O	11	Oak
Lough Eske	Greenan	66319J	7	Oak
Lough Owel	Newcastle	73104A	1	Oak
Lough Owel	Newcastle	73106N	1	Oak
Lough Owel	Newcastle	73115M	1	Oak
Monaghan	Dartrey	71561N	1	Oak
Monaghan	Derrygorry	72211K	2	Oak
Mountbellew	Demesne	55662K	1	Oak
Mullinavat	Brownstown	21525Q	1	Oak
Portumna	Demesne	55854P	2	Oak
Shillelagh	Coolatin	16139K	1	Oak
Swanlinbar	Oakwood	71130S	6	Oak
Swanlinbar	Derinish Beg	71836I	11	Oak
Virginia	Demesne	71010O	6	Oak
Virginia	Headfort	71016H	1	Oak
Virginia	Headfort	71020I	1	Oak
Woodford	Rosturra	56178B	5	Oak
Dungarvan	Dromana	27158J	4	Sycamore
Graiguenamanagh	Mount Loftus	21279K	5	Sycamore
Kilsheelan	Glen	23607S	8	Sycamore
Midleton	Ballyannan	31814U	1	Sycamore
Monaghan	Rossmore	72101A	9	Sycamore
Monaghan	Rossmore	72101A	11	Sycamore
Monaghan	Rossmore	72105D	3	Sycamore
Mullinavat	Mountain Grove	21609B	1	Sycamore
Mullinavat	Mountain Grove	21609B	12	Sycamore
Newmarket	Knockaclarg	36279H	5	Sycamore

P/YEAR	STOCKING	TOP HEIGHT	DBH	ELEVATION	SOILTYPE
	trees/ha	m	cm	m	
1807	175	16	50	30	Podzol
1807	175	16	46	60	Podzol
1880	100	15	50	50	Grey brown podzolic
1850	70	22	65	45	Peat
1850	250	20	50	26	Podzol
1850	250	20	55	30	Podzol
1910	400	22	32	7	Brown podzolic
1950	1000	16	15	70	Gley
1935	500	22	30	150	Grey brown podzolic Brown earth
1936	400	18	30	200	Brown earth
1850	200	20	70	160	Brown earth
1900	60	20	70	65	Brown earth
1949	500	18	22	90	Brown earth
1870	40	25	80	90	Acid brown earth
1820	100	23	60	90	Acid brown earth
1830	100	18	55	90	Podzol
1850	300	10	35	60	Grey brown podzolic
1830	150	22	60	40	Grey brown podzolic
1830	100	20	40	85	Podzol
1870	250	22	50	60	Gley/Podzol/Brown podzolic*
1940	600	18	25	90	Brown earth
1923	260	22	23	90	Podzol
1850	175	24	40	140	Brown podzolic
1880	250	18	34	120	Podzol
1858	40	20	45	75	Acid brown earth
1833	300	20	40	75	Acid brown earth
1833	100	22	60	150	Acid brown earth
1870	350	22	40	180	Podzol
1810	150	22	55	30	Podzol
1782	35	23	75	90	Grey brown podzolic
1782	250	23	55	120	Grey brown podzolic
1782	100	20	60	110	Grey brown podzolic
1782	150	25	55	90	Gley
1840	30	20	55	30	Gley
1820	100	17	55	30	Podzol
1936	300	17	33	55	Brown earth
1936	300	18	25	55	Brown earth
1936	200	17	28	55	Brown earth
1820	120	25	55	85	Gley
1894	150	23	50	85	Gley
1941	700	16	20	65	Grey brown podzolic
1830	300	16	30	100	Brown podzolic
1900	120	20	60	45	Grey brown podzolic
1972	1200	8	8	150	Brown podzolic
1820	100	23	75	80	Brown earth
1936	300	20	33	55	Gley
1937	600	18	28	180	Brown earth
1938	450	22	25	95	Brown earth
1938	400	20	29	90	Brown podzolic
1887	150	23	60	45	Brown earth
1930	700	18	28	60	Brown earth
1937	100	24	50	40	Brown earth
1956	220	27	30	30	Brown podzolic
1950	700	20	30	14	Brown earth
1925	100	25	55	90	Brown earth
1925	100	23	45	90	Gley
1922	300	25	34	100	Brown earth
1910	60	18	35	50	Acid brown earth
1963	700	17	19	30	Acid brown earth
1968	2500	4	-	250	Gley

Index

....